Britain's Changing Environment

Garrett Nagle

Nelson

Contents

Chapter 1
Britain's changing climate

In this chapter we examine basic atmospheric processes, and look at the factors affecting Britain's climate. It is important to consider the global atmospheric scale, since Britain's weather is very much dependent upon her global location. The earth's atmosphere is constantly changing. It varies day by day, season by season, and over a period of decades, centuries and millennia. The weather we experience is the result of large-scale factors, such as the general circulation of the atmosphere, and small-scale factors, such as aspect and land use. After considering atmospheric processes, we concentrate on Britain's changing climate and, in particular, urban climates.

WHAT CAUSES THE 'WEATHER'?

In order to understand Britain's weather and the climatic changes that are taking place, it is important to consider basic atmospheric features and processes. This will allow us to understand more fully the pattern of weather and climate that is experienced across Britain. The term 'climate' refers to the state of the atmosphere, for example temperature, rainfall, winds, humidity, cloud cover and pressure, over a period of not less than thirty years. It refers to the averages of these variables and to the extremes as well. By contrast, the term 'weather' refers to the state of the atmosphere at any particular moment in time. Generally, we look at the weather over a period of a few days, considering the same variables as for climate.

ATMOSPHERIC COMPOSITION

The main gases in dry (unsaturated) air are nitrogen (78.1%), oxygen (20.9%) and argon (0.93%). Other gases include helium, ozone, hydrogen and methane. Some of these minor gases play a crucial role, for example carbon dioxide (CO_2) absorbs heat, allowing the lower parts of the atmosphere to be heated. Since 1945 there has been a 10% increase in atmospheric CO_2 content – this upward trend matches closely the global rise of temperature during this period (Figure 1.1).

The atmosphere also contains solid matter and water. Solids such as dust, pollution and salt allow condensation to occur. This can cause cloud formation and precipitation. The more solid particles there are in the air, the greater the potential for cloud formation and rain (and other forms of precipitation). Water vapour is held in the lower ten to fifteen kilometres of the atmosphere. At higher altitudes, the air is too cold to hold water (warmer air has a greater capacity to hold moisture than cold air) and there is not enough turbulence/mixing to carry vapour upwards. Water vapour is also important in the absorption of heat – in areas with cloud cover, night-time temperatures are increased but daytime ones are reduced.

ATMOSPHERIC ENERGY

The atmosphere is an open energy system receiving energy from the sun as well as a little from the earth itself (Figure 1.2). This amount is relatively small but locally very important, as we will see in the case of urban heat islands (see pages 23–27). Incoming solar radiation is referred to as **insolation**.

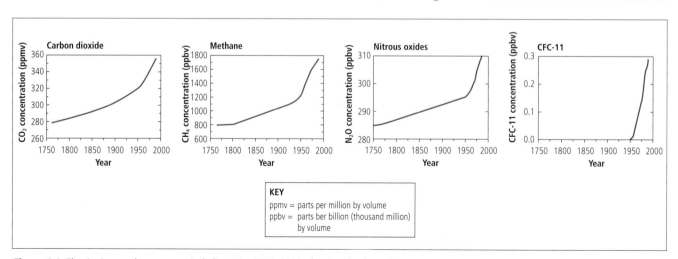

KEY
ppmv = parts per million by volume
ppbv = parts ber billion (thousand million) by volume

Figure 1.1 *The rise in greenhouse gases, including CO$_2$, 1750–2000, showing the dramatic increase since the 1950s*
Source: Digby, B., 1994, The physical environment, Heinemann

The atmosphere constantly receives energy, yet until recently, the world was not getting any hotter, i.e. there was a balance between inputs (insolation) and outputs (**reradiation**). Balance is achieved in three main ways:

- radiation – electro-magnetic waves such as X-ray, micro- and short-wave radiation from the sun, and long-wave from the earth
- convection – the transfer of heat by the movement of a gas or liquid
- conduction – the transfer of heat by contact.
  Of the incoming radiation:
- 17% is absorbed by atmospheric gases, especially oxygen and ozone at high altitudes, and CO_2 and water vapour at low altitudes
- scattering by particles accounts for a net loss of 6%
- clouds and water droplets reflect 23% (this can be as much as 80% of total insolation in some places)
- generally about 7% is reflected from the surface.

The term **albedo** refers to the reflectivity of the earth's surface. The earth's albedo accounts for 36% of insolation. As gases absorb 17% of incoming insolation, only 47% of the insolation at the top of the atmosphere (the tropopause) actually gets through to the earth's surface (and is not reflected back).

Terrestrial Reradiation

Energy received by the earth is reradiated. Of this, 8% passes out into space. Much energy is absorbed by clouds and reradiated back to earth. Evaporation and condensation account for a heat loss of 23%, some of which is carried up by turbulence. Thus, terrestrial heat gained by the atmosphere amounts to 39 units. In fact, the atmosphere is heated predominantly from below, with most of the incoming short-wave solar radiation passing through the atmosphere without heating it, and the out-going long-wave radiation being trapped by CO_2.

TEMPERATURE AT GROUND LEVEL

A number of factors affect temperatures over the globe. The most important is latitude (Figure 1.3, see page 6). At the equator there is a great amount of insolation; at high latitudes less energy is received, owing to the thickness of the atmosphere and the oblique approach of the sun's rays. Length of day and season are also important factors – the longer the sun shines, the greater the amount of insolation received. The long days experienced at the poles for several months of the year, when the sun never sets, may compensate, in part, for the low level of insolation received. However, during the long polar winter nights, vast amounts of energy are lost. The result of the different levels of insolation around the globe is an imbalance – energy gain in the tropics and energy loss at the poles. As neither region gets progressively hotter or colder, it means that heat and energy is transferred from the equator to the poles by winds and ocean currents, thus maintaining the status quo.

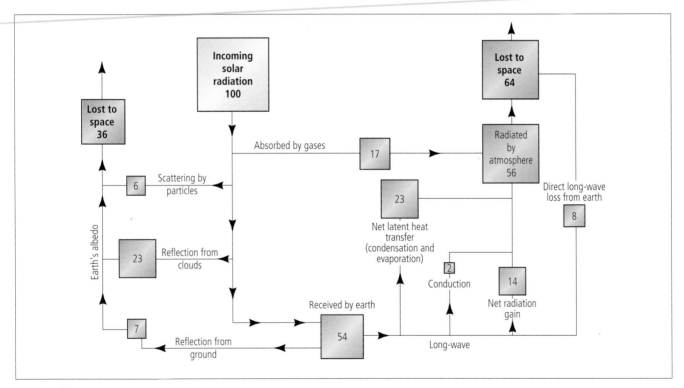

Figure 1.2 *The earth's atmospheric energy budget*
Source: Bryant, R., 1979, Physical geography, Made Simple Books

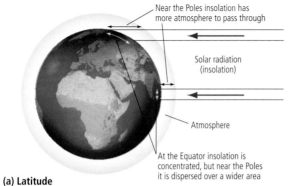

(a) Latitude

Areas that are close to the equator receive more heat than areas that are close to the poles. This is due to two causes:

1 incoming solar radiation (insolation) is concentrated near the equator, but dispersed near the poles
2 insolation near the poles has to pass through a greater amount of atmosphere and there is more chance of it being reflected back out to space.

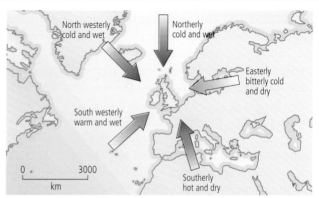

(b) Prevailing winds

A prevailing wind is the wind that blows most frequently in an area. The effect of the prevailing wind depends upon the origin of the wind. For example, the prevailing winds from the south west that affect the British Isles. bring warm air from the mid-Atlantic. By contrast, north-east winds from Siberia bring bitterly cold conditions in winter.

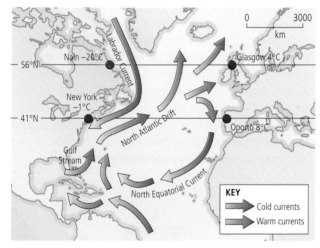

(c) Ocean currents

The effect of an ocean current depends upon whether it is a warm current or a cold one. Warm currents move away from the Equator, whereas cold currents move towards it. The cold Labrador Current reduces the temperature on the western side of the Atlantic, whilst the warm North Atlantic Drift raises the temperatures on the eastern side.

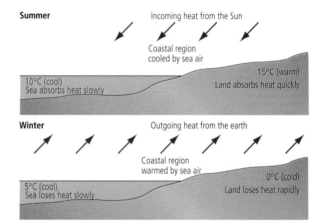

(d) Distance from the sea

It takes more energy to heat up water than it does to heat land. However, it takes longer for water to lose heat. Hence, land is hotter than the sea by day, but colder than the sea by night. Places that are close to the sea are cool by day, but mild by night. With increasing distance from the sea, this effect is reduced.

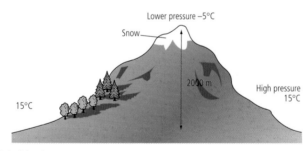

(e) Altitude

Temperatures decrease with altitude. On average it drops about 1°C for every 100 metres. That means 10°C over 1000m. This is because air at higher altitudes is thinner and less dense.

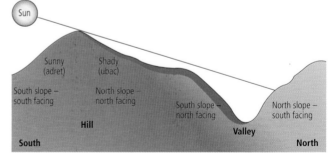

(f) Aspect

Aspect is the direction a place faces. On a local scale aspect is very important. In the British Isles south facing places are warmer than north and east facing places.

Figure 1.3 *Factors affecting temperature*
Source: Nagle, G., 1998, Geography through diagrams, OUP

	J	F	M	A	M	J	J	A	S	O	N	D
Eastbourne	7.3	7.1	9.1	11.5	14.9	17.8	19.7	20.0	18.1	15.0	10.8	8.5
Gatwick	6.7	7.1	9.9	12.6	16.3	19.6	21.7	21.4	18.8	15.0	10.1	7.7

Figure 1.4 *Mean monthly temperatures for a coastal and an inland location*

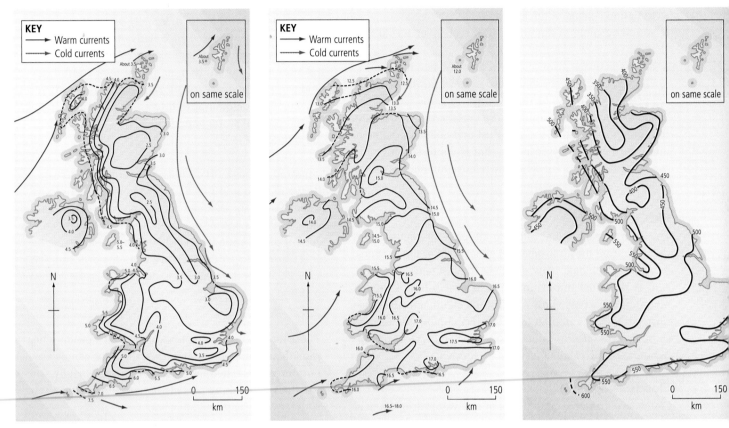

Figure 1.5 *Mean monthly air temperatures (°c) in January and July for Britain*
Source: Goudie, A., and Brunsden, D., 1994, The environment of the British Isles, an atlas, OUP

Figure 1.6 *Potential evaporation (mm) in Britain*
Source: Goudie, A., and Brunsden, D., 1994, The environment of the British Isles,

QUESTION

1 Study Figure 1.5 which shows mean monthly air temperatures in January and July for the UK.

a) Describe how temperature varies in **(i)** January and **(ii)** July across the United Kingdom.

b) Using the information in Figure 1.3, explain the differences you have noted in **(a) (i)** and **(ii)**. Use data from Figures 1.4 and 1.5 to support your answer.

EVAPORATION AND CONDENSATION

Six hundred calories of heat are needed to change 1 gram of water from a liquid to a vapour. During evaporation, water is converted from a liquid state to a gaseous state (water vapour) by heat. Evaporation cools 1 kilogram of air by 2.5°C. When condensation occurs, latent heat locked in the water vapour is released, causing a rise in temperature.

Evaporation occurs when the vapour pressure of a water surface exceeds that in the atmosphere. (Vapour pressure is the pressure exerted by the water vapour present in the atmosphere.) The maximum vapour pressure at any temperature occurs when the air is saturated (see Inset 1.1 Humidity on page 8). Evaporation aims to equalise the pressures. It depends on three main factors:

- initial humidity of the air – if air is very dry, strong evaporation occurs; if it is saturated, very little occurs
- supply of heat – the hotter the air, the more evaporation takes place
- wind strength – under calm conditions, the air becomes saturated rapidly.

Geographers frequently use the term **potential evapotranspiration** (Figure 1.6). This is the amount of water that would be evaporated if there were an unlimited supply of water. In most cases, there is not an unlimited supply – so, for example, in East Anglia actual evaporation rates are between 400 and 500 mm per annum – if more water were supplied, the evaporation rate would rise to between 500 and 600 mm.

Condensation occurs when either (a) enough water vapour is evaporated into an air mass for it to become saturated or (b) when the temperature drops so that **dew point** (the temperature at which air is saturated) is reached. The first is relatively rare, the second common. Air cooling occurs in three main ways:

- radiation cooling of the air
- contact cooling of the air when it rests over a cold surface
- adiabatic (expansive) cooling of the air when it rises.

Condensation is very difficult to achieve in pure air as it requires tiny particles or nuclei onto which the vapour can condense. In the lower atmosphere these particles are quite common, for example, sea salt, dust and pollution. Some of these particles are hygroscopic, that is water-seeking, and condensation may occur when the relative humidity is as low as 80%.

PRECIPITATION

The term 'precipitation' refers to all forms of deposition of moisture from the atmosphere in either solid or liquid states. It includes rain, hail, snow, and dew. In most parts of Britain, rain is the most important form of precipitation, but in mountainous areas snow can also be significant. Because rain is the most common form of precipitation, the term is sometimes applied to rainfall alone. For any type of precipitation to occur, clouds must first be formed.

Clouds

Clouds are formed from millions of tiny water droplets held in suspension. Clouds are classified in a number of ways, the most important being:

- form or shape, for example, stratiform (layered) and cumuliform (heaped)
- height – low (less than 2000 metres), middle or alto (2000–7000 metres) and high (7000–13 000 metres). There are a number of different types of clouds (Figure 1.7).
- High clouds consist mostly of ice crystals. Cirrus are wispy clouds and include cirrocumulus (mackerel sky) and cirrostratus (halo effect around the sun or moon). The weather associated with high clouds is generally sunny and dry.
- Alto or middle height clouds generally consist of water drops. The weather, although cloudy, is generally dry. They exist in temperatures of less than 0°C.
- Low clouds indicate poor weather, bringing rainfall. Stratus clouds are dense, grey and low-lying. Nimbostratus are those which produce rain (nimbus means storm). Stratocumulus are long cloud rolls – a mixture of stratus and cumulus. With upward air movement, associated with warm temperatures, clouds develop vertically, in some cases reaching from low to middle height.

Inset 1.1
Humidity

Absolute humidity refers to the amount of water in the atmosphere. For example, there may be eight grams of water in a cubic metre of air. **Relative humidity** (RH) refers to the water vapour present expressed as a percentage of the maximum amount that air at that temperature can hold. For example, air at 20°C can hold up to 17.117 g/cm^3 of water vapour. If air at that temperature contains only 8.5585 g/cm^3 of water vapour, its RH is 8.5585/17.117 × 100% or 50% RH.

Saturated air has a RH of 100%. If there is no increase in the water vapour in the air, as air temperature rises, its RH decreases. For example, air at 4.4°C may be saturated with as little as 4g/cm^3 of water. As the air is warmed, the amount of moisture it can hold increases. Hence, as the air is warmed to 10°C its relative humidity drops to 71%, at 15.5°C its RH drops to 51% and at 32°C its RH is down to 19%.

These include cumulonimbus clouds which produce heavy rainfall and often thunderstorms. Cumulus clouds are flat bottomed and heaped. They indicate bright, brisk weather, with sunny periods between the clouds, windy with isolated scattered showers.

The factors affecting cloud formation are:

- unstable conditions – the dominant form of uplift is convection and this may cause cumulus clouds
- stable conditions – stratiform clouds generally occur
- weather fronts – a variety of clouds exist
- relief or topography – stratiform or cumuliform clouds are caused, depending on stability of the air.

Banner clouds are formed by orographic uplift (that is, air forced to rise, over a mountain for example) under stable air conditions. Uplifted moist airstreams may condense only at the very summit, where they form a small cloud in the lee of the summit. Beyond the summit, the air sinks and the cloud disappears. Wave clouds are small, regular clouds found downstream of the hill as the main cloud disappears.

Fog

Fog is cloud at ground level. Radiation fog is formed in low-lying areas during calm weather, especially during spring and autumn. The surface of the ground, cooled rapidly at night by radiation, cools the air immediately above it. This air then flows into hollows by gravity and is cooled to dew point, so causing condensation. Ideal conditions include a

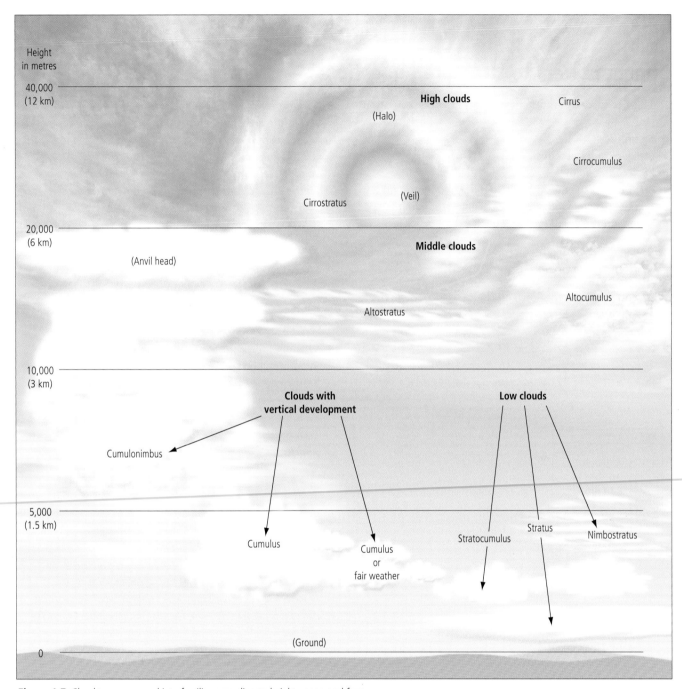

Figure 1.7 *Cloud types, grouped into families according to height, range and form*
Source: Barry, R. and Chorley, R., 1987, Atmosphere, weather and climate

surface layer of moist air and clear skies to allow maximum radiation to occur quickly. As the sun rises, radiation fog clears away. Under cold anticyclonic conditions in late autumn and winter, fog may be thicker and more persistent, and around large towns smog may develop under an inversion layer. A **temperature inversion** is where cold air is found at ground level with warm air above it – unlike the normal conditions in which air temperature declines with height.

Advection fog is formed when warm moist air flows horizontally over a cooler land or sea surface. The decrease in temperature of the lower layers of the air causes it to go below the dew point. With fairly light winds, the fog forms close to the water surface, but with stronger turbulence, the condensed layer may be uplifted to form a low stratus sheet.

Steam fog is very localised where cold air blows over much warmer water. Evaporation from the water quickly saturates the air and the resulting condensation leads to steaming. It occurs when very cold polar air meets relatively warm water.

Skills:
Short answers to structured questions

The keys to success in short answers and structured questions are to:
- be precise
- use geographical terms
- keep to the point
- don't repeat the question (there is not enough room)
- follow the command words (see Skills: Responding to command words in Chapter 2, page 32).

1 Define the term 'fog'. (1 mark)
Fog is cloud at ground level.

2 Describe the pattern shown on Figure 1.8. (3 marks)
Most fog occurs inland. The main concentration of fog is in the industrial areas from Sheffield south to the Midlands. There are also high levels of fog along the M4 and M3 corridors. There is a high frequency of fog along the industrialised parts of the Clyde valley in Scotland. By contrast, there is a low frequency of fog in coastal areas.

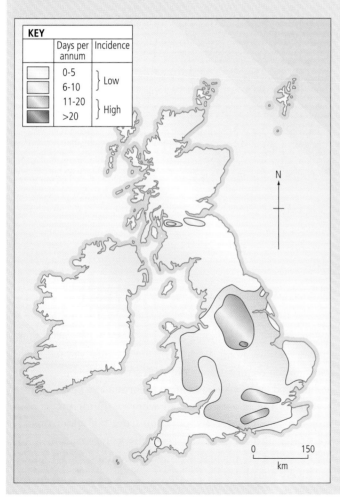

KEY

	Days per annum	Incidence
	0-5	Low
	6-10	Low
	11-20	High
	>20	High

N

0 150 km

3 Suggest reasons for the high incidence of fog in the areas indicated. (3 marks)
In the industrial areas, emissions of SO_2 act as condensation nuclei and allow fog to form. Along the motorways the heavy concentration of vehicle emissions does the same. By contrast, in coastal areas the higher minimum temperatures mean that condensation during high pressure conditions is less likely.

4 Why is fog common in anticyclonic conditions? (3 marks)
Anticyclones are high pressure systems and characterised by clear skies and low wind speeds. Clear skies allow maximum cooling by night. Air is rapidly cooled to dew point, condensation occurs and fog is formed.

5 Why does fog commonly occur over the sea in autumn and spring? (4 marks)
The contrast in temperature between land and sea is significant. Warm air from over the sea is cooled when it moves onto the land during anticyclonic conditions. In summer, the sea is cooler than the land, so air is not cooled when it blows onto the land. By contrast, in winter there are more low pressure systems, causing higher winds and mixing of the air. This fog is more frequent in autumn and spring.

6 In what ways can human activity lead to an increase in the incidence of fog? (3 marks)
Industries emit large volumes of pollution, such as SO_2, which encourage condensation to occur. The burning of coal in domestic homes helped form the 'pea-soupers' of London in the 1950s. In the 1990s vehicle emissions have replaced industrial emissions and coal burning as the main source of pollution which causes fog and smog.

7 What problems does fog pose for human activities? . (3 marks)
During fog, visibility is reduced to less than 1 kilometre. This makes driving and flying aeroplanes hazardous. In addition, fogs in winter can be accompanied by freezing conditions. Freezing fog frequently results in accidents on motorways and large pile ups.

***Figure 1.8** Incidence of fog days over the British Isles*
Source: Edexcel, 1997

Rainfall

When minute droplets of water are condensed from water vapour they float in the atmosphere as clouds. If droplets coalesce they form large droplets which, when heavy enough to overcome by gravity an ascending current, fall as rain. Therefore cloud droplets must reach a certain size (and therefore weight) to form rain. There are a number of theories to suggest how rain drops are formed.

The Bergeron theory suggests that for rain to form, water and ice must exist together in clouds at temperatures below 0°C. Water droplets and ice crystals contain a nucleus – water has a hygroscopic (water seeking/holding) nucleus, such as dust, smoke, SO_2, NaCl or fine soil. These enable the water vapour to stay as water vapour at low temperatures. Below 0ºC ice particles have a greater relative humidity than liquids (they contain more moisture). But between –5ºC and –25ºC, vapour pressure is greater over water than ice. The result is that the ice crystals grow at the expense of water droplets as water vapour condenses onto the ice by sublimation.

As ice crystals grow they become big enough to overcome turbulence and cloud updrafts, and fall. As they fall, crystals coalesce to form larger snow flakes. The snow and ice melt and become rain as they fall to lower altitudes where the temperatures are above freezing.

Other mechanisms must also exist, because rain also comes from clouds which are not as cold. Mechanisms include:

- condensation on extra large hygroscopic nuclei
- coalescence by sweeping, whereby a falling droplet sweeps up others in its path
- the growth of droplets by electrical attraction.

Rain and drizzle are found when the temperature is more than 0°C (drizzle has a diameter of less than 0.5 millimetres). Sleet is partially melted snow and hail is alternate concentric rings of clear and opaque ice, formed by being carried up and down in vertical air currents in large cumulonimbus clouds. Freezing and partial melting may occur several times before the pellet is large enough to fall from the cloud.

Types of rainfall

In the British Isles, the pattern of rainfall is complicated (Figure 1.9, see page 12). It is influenced by the general circulation of the atmosphere. High rainfall is associated with south westerly winds and low pressure system (cyclone or depression) tracks (the path of a low pressure system). Low rainfall is found where there is subsiding air. Mountain ranges also affect rainfall: in most mountains high rainfall occurs on the windward side and rain shadows are formed on the lee side. Altitude is important especially on a local scale. In general, there are increases of precipitation to about two kilometres up from sea level. Above this level, rainfall decreases because the air temperature is so low. In parts of south-east England, and especially over London, convectional thunderstorms are also important (Figure 1.10).

Thunderstorms

Thunderstorms are special cases of rapid cloud formation and heavy precipitation in unstable air conditions. Absolute or conditional instability exists to great heights, causing strong updraughts to develop within cumulonimbus clouds. Thunderstorms are especially common in tropical and warm areas where air can hold large amounts of water.

Several stages can be identified:

1 Developing stage: updraught caused by uplift; energy (latent heat) is released as condensation occurs; air becomes very unstable; rainfall occurs as cloud; temperature is greater than 0°C; the great strength of uplift prevents snow and ice from falling

2 Mature stage: sudden onset of heavy rain and maybe thunder and lightning; rainfall drags cold air down with it; upper parts of the cloud may reach the tropopause (the boundary between the troposphere – the lowest layer of the atmosphere – and the stratosphere – the region of the atmosphere 8–16 kilometres high where temperature does not fall as altitude increases); the cloud spreads giving the characteristic anvil shape

3 Dissipating stage: downdraughts prevent any further convective instability; the new cells may be initiated by the meeting of cold downdraughts from cells some distance apart, triggering the rise of warm air in between. (A convection cell includes rising air – stage 1 and sinking air – stage 3. The whole process forms a cell of rising and sinking air.)

Lightning occurs to relieve the tension between differently charged areas, for example, between cloud and ground or within the cloud itself, i.e. where the upper parts of the cloud are positive and the lower parts are negative, with the very base of the cloud being positively charged. The origin of the charges is not very clear, although is thought to be due to condensation and evaporation. Thunder occurs as lightning heats the air to cause very high temperatures. Rapid expansion and vibration of the column produces thunder.

QUESTION

1 Figure 1.10 (on page 13) shows the distribution of thunder over part of southern Britain. Describe the pattern shown on the map. How do you explain this distribution?

Types of rainfall

Convectional rainfall

When the land becomes very hot, it heats the air above it. This air expands and rises. As it rises, cooling and condensation take place. If it continues to rise, rain will fall. It is very common in tropical areas. In Britain it is quite common in the summer, especially in the south-east.

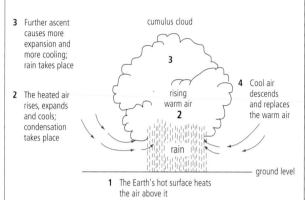

3 Further ascent causes more expansion and more cooling; rain takes place

2 The heated air rises, expands and cools; condensation takes place

cumulus cloud

3

rising warm air

2

rain

4 Cool air descends and replaces the warm air

ground level

1 The Earth's hot surface heats the air above it

Frontal or cyclonic rainfall

Frontal rain occurs when warm air meets cold air. The warm air, being lighter and less dense, is forced to rise over the cold, denser air. As it rises it cools, condenses and forms rain.

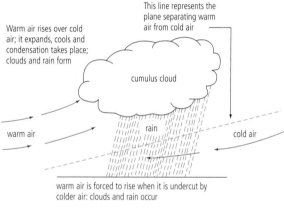

Warm air rises over cold air; it expands, cools and condensation takes place; clouds and rain form

This line represents the plane separating warm air from cold air

cumulus cloud

warm air

rain

cold air

warm air is forced to rise when it is undercut by colder air: clouds and rain occur

Relief or orographic rainfall

Air may be forced to rise over a barrier such as a mountain. As it rises it cools, condenses and forms rain. There is often a rain shadow effect, whereby the lee slope receives a relatively small amount of rain.

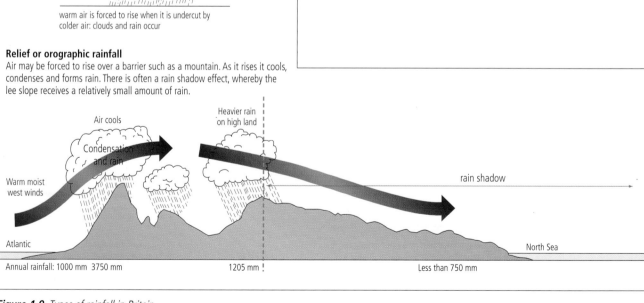

Air cools

Condensation and rain

Heavier rain on high land

Warm moist west winds

rain shadow

Atlantic

North Sea

Annual rainfall: 1000 mm 3750 mm   1205 mm   Less than 750 mm

Rainfall in Britain

There is a great variation in the amount, type and seasonal nature of rainfall in Britain.

- The heaviest rainfall is over highland areas such as Wales, the Lake District and the Scottish Highlands. Much of this is relief rainfall.
- Rainfall is heavier in the west than the east. Much of this is frontal rain driven across the country by prevailing winds.
- The south east of England experiences more convectional rainfall in summer than elsewhere in Britain, because it is the hottest part of the country (it is low-lying and also less affected by North Atlantic Drift).

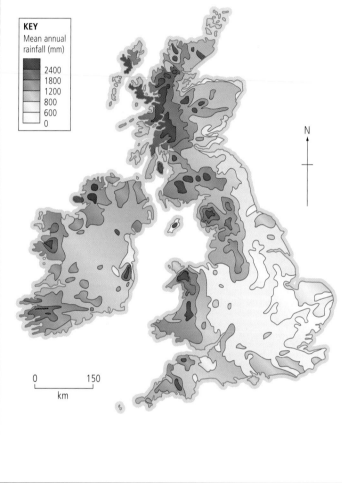

KEY
Mean annual rainfall (mm)

2400
1800
1200
800
600
0

N

0   150
km

Figure 1.9 *Types of rainfall in Britain*
Source: Nagle, G., 1998, Geography through diagrams, OUP

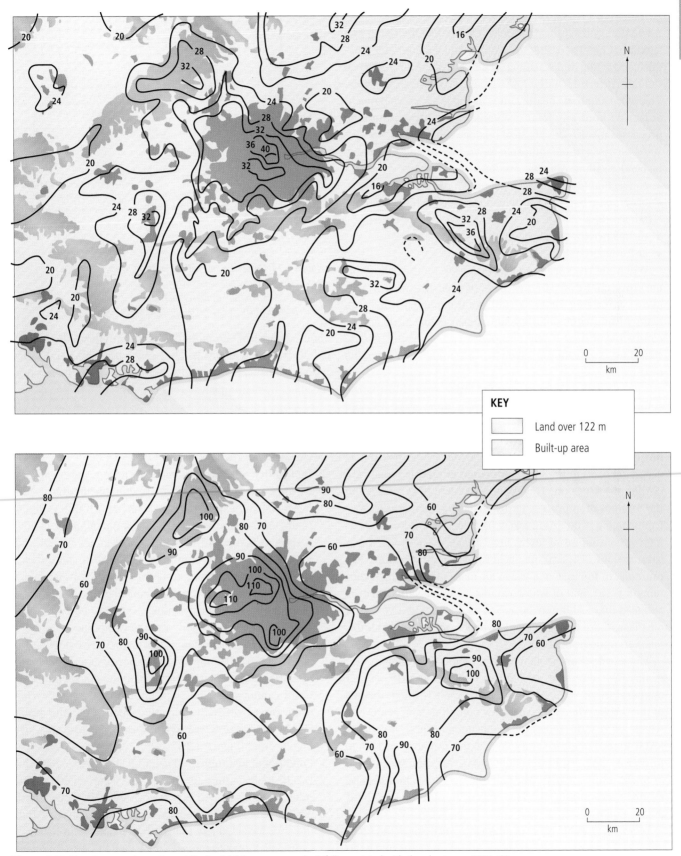

Figure 1.10 *Thunderstorms in south-east England (a) Average annual rainfall associated with thunderstorms, 1951–60, measured in inches and (b) Average annual number of days with thunder, 1951–60*
Source: Goudie, A., 1993, The human impact on the natural environment, Blackwell

ADIABATIC PROCESSES

Adiabatic processes are those which relate to the rising and sinking of air. The rising (expanding and cooling) and sinking (contracting and warming) of air causes the air to change temperature internally, i.e. without any other influence. Therefore adiabatic heating and cooling is an internal mechanism without any heat exchange. By contrast, diabatic processes involve the physical mixing of air.

As air rises in the atmosphere it is cooled and there may be condensation. Air may rise for four reasons:

- convection (caused by the heating of the ground below)
- orographic barriers (air forced to rise over hills or mountains)
- turbulence (in the air flow)
- at frontal systems.

When air rises from one elevation to another, the temperature changes. The decrease of pressure with height allows the rising air to expand. As it expands, it uses up energy from within and becomes cooler (since air is a poor conductor of heat it will not gain any heat from the surrounding atmosphere). Likewise, when air sinks, it gains heat by contraction.

The normal or **environmental lapse rate** (ELR) is the actual temperature decline with height, on average 6°C/km.

Adiabatic cooling and warming in dry (unsaturated) air occurs at a rate of 10°C/km. This is known as the **dry adiabatic lapse rate** (DALR). Air in which condensation is occurring cools at the lower **saturated adiabatic lapse rate** (SALR) of 4°–9°C/km. This is because latent heat released in the condensation process partly offsets the temperature loss from cooling. The SALR varies between 4°–9°C/km according to the amount of latent heat released – less for warm saturated air (4°C/km) than cold saturated air (9°C/km). For example, in the case of a warm air mass of 27°C which contains a great deal of water vapour, so much latent heat is released that SALR may be as low as 4°C/km. In a very cold air mass, there may be so little water vapour that SALR differs very little from DALR.

Lapse rates can be shown on a temperature/height diagram. The example in Figure 1.11 shows air with a temperature of 20°C. At first, when the air is lifted, it cools at the DALR. When it reaches dew point (the temperature at which air is saturated and condensation occurs), it cools at SALR. Once the air is saturated (relative humidity of 100%), further cooling results in condensation. Air continues to rise at SALR until it reaches the same temperature and density as the surrounding air. This marks the top of the cloud development.

A very noticeable effect of adiabatic processes is the Föhn effect that occurs in the European Alps. Winds approach the Alps as very warm moist air streams, rise, quickly reach condensation level, and therefore cool at SALR. At the summit most of the moisture is already lost. On descent, winds warm up at DALR. They reach the plains and valleys as hot winds with low relative humidity and can have a drastic effect by melting snow very rapidly.

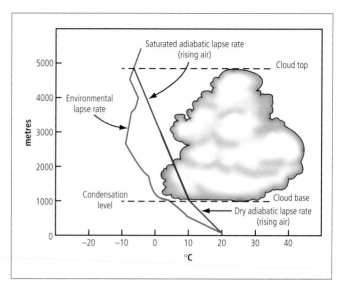

Figure 1.11 *Unstable air conditions, with air rising, first at the DALR and then at the SALR. Ascent ceases when the rising air has the same temperature and density as the surrounding air*
Source: Bryant, R., 1979, Physical geography, Made Simple Books

ATMOSPHERIC STABILITY AND INSTABILITY

Air stability and instability refers to the buoyancy characteristics of air.

1 **Instability** – Instability occurs where a parcel of air is warmer and therefore less dense than the air above, causing rising and expansion. Air is unstable if ELR is greater than DALR, as on Figure 1.12. If a parcel of air is lifted, it rises at DALR and immediately becomes warmer and lighter than its surroundings. It therefore continues to rise. Unstable air tends to occur on very hot days when the ground layers are heated considerably. If the unstable air is sufficiently moist, strong vertical cloud development and possibly rainfall will occur.

2 **Stability** – Stable air conditions (stability) exist when ELR is less than DALR and SALR. If a parcel of air is displaced upwards, it immediately gets cooler and denser and sinks. Uplift cannot be sustained. Conditions in an anticyclone (high pressure) with subsiding air are usually stable. Stable air will only rise when forced, for example, over high ground (Figure 1.13).

3 **Conditional instability** – When ELR lies between SALR and DALR, moist saturated air will rise whereas dry unsaturated air will sink. Air is therefore stable in respect to the dry rate and would normally sink to its original level. But if the air is forced to rise to higher elevations, thus becoming saturated, it may become warmer than the surrounding air and would continue to rise of its own accord. Under these circumstances, air is unstable only if it is saturated.

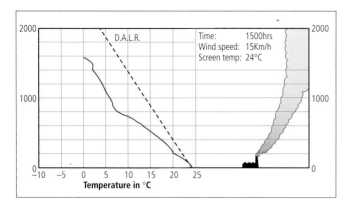

Figure 1.12 *Unstable air*

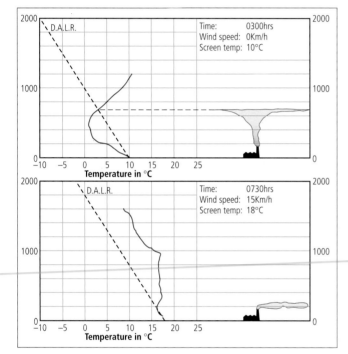

Figure 1.13 *Stable air*

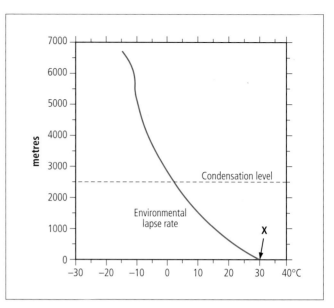

Figure 1.14 *Environmental lapse rate (ELR) for a particular time and place*
Source: 1984, University of London

Figure 1.16 *Clouds over mountains on the west coast of Ireland*

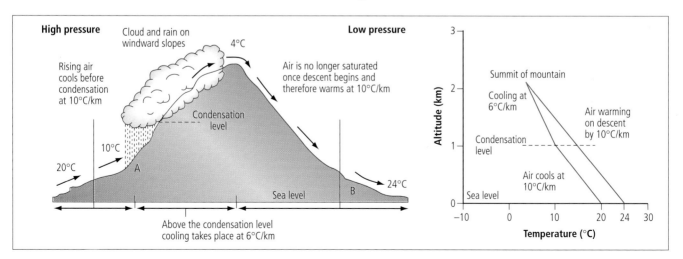

Figure 1.15 *Air flow over a mountain*
Source: 1984, University of London

QUESTIONS

1 Study Figure 1.14 which shows an environmental lapse rate.

a) At what height will a parcel of air rising from the ground level at **X** become stable? (Assume the DALR is 10°C per 1000 metres **and** the SALR is 5°C per 1000 metres.)

b) What is the significance of the 'condensation level'?

c) Suggest **three** different causes of the initial uplift of the parcel of air.

2 Study figures 1.15 and 1.16 which show the flow of air over a mountain.

a) Why does air not continue to rise on the lee side of the mountain?

b) State **two** differences between the air at **A** and the air at **B**. Explain both of these differences.

c) Suggest **two** consequences of this airstream modification for the weather on the lee side of the mountain.

AIR MOTION

Vertical air motion is important on a local scale, whereas horizontal motion (wind) is important at all scales from small-scale eddies to global wind systems. The basic cause of air motion is the unequal heating of the earth's surface. Variable heating of the earth causes variations in air pressure and this in turn sets the air in motion – the transfer of heat by air movement is the main method of equalising heat variations. There is thus a strong correlation between winds and air pressure.

Pressure gradient

Pressure differentials are the basic cause of air motion. The pressure gradient force (PGF) causes air to move from high pressure (HP) to low pressure (LP) (Figure 1.17). The strength of the wind varies with the difference in pressure. The closer the isobars, the steeper the gradient. In theory, winds should blow at right angles to the isobars, but in practice they are affected by a number of forces, such as the Coriolis effect, centripetal and centrifugal forces, and friction.

Coriolis effect

The Coriolis effect is the deflection of moving objects, including water and air masses, caused by the rotation of the earth; nearer the equator the effect of the Coriolis force is slight, whereas at the poles it is great. In the northern hemisphere the deflection is to the right, in the southern hemisphere it is to the left (Figure 1.17). The degree of deflection of winds varies with the speed of the moving air, as well as with latitude. The faster the wind, and thus the more ground covered in a given time, the greater the effect of the Coriolis force.

Geostrophic winds

Global winds tend to blow with steady force and duration. PGF winds blow from HP to LP while the effect of the Coriolis force is to produce circular movement around the globe.

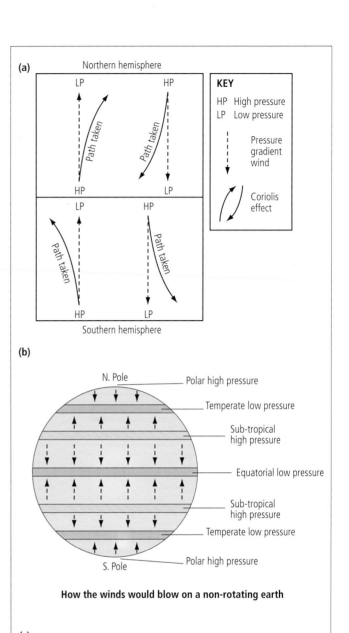

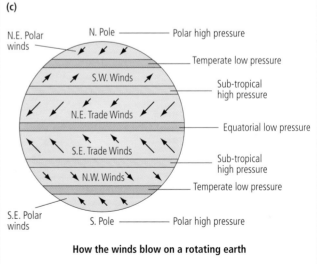

Figure 1.17 *Pressure gradient and Coriolis force*
Source: Bunnett, R.,1987, Physical geography in diagrams, Longman

Winds adopt a balance between the PGF and the Coriolis force. The resulting winds are known as **geostrophic winds**.

Centripetal and centrifugal forces

Winds are also affected by centripetal and centrifugal forces. In low pressure systems air blows inwards and anticlockwise (centripetal force) whereas in high pressure systems air blows outwards and clockwise (centrifugal force). In 1857 Buy Ballot, a Dutch meteorologist, showed that in the northern hemisphere if you stand with your back to the wind, low pressure is on your left and high pressure is on your right. The reverse is true in the southern hemisphere.

Friction

Below 750 metres, friction also has an effect on the balance of the forces affecting wind movement. It reduces wind speed and therefore reduces the effect of the Coriolis force. Thus, the PGF causes air movement to flow towards low pressure and the resultant winds blow at a slight angle to the isobars. The effect of friction is much reduced over smooth surfaces, especially the oceans. It is of less importance during strong windy conditions than during calmer spells.

Jet streams and thermal winds

Jet streams are concentrated bands of rapid air movement which occur near the top of the tropopause. They are intense thermal winds caused by the difference in temperature between two air masses (Figure 1.18). Jet streams occur in two zones – one in the sub-tropics and the other, the Polar Jet Stream, associated with the low pressure of the mid-latitudes.

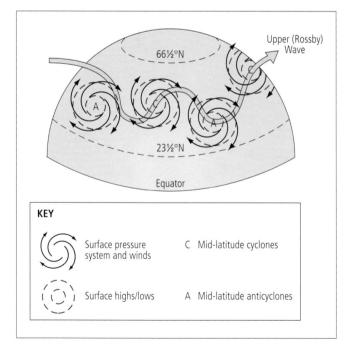

Figure 1.18 *Mid-latitude winds and pressure systems*

The meandering path of the thermal winds and jet streams is known as the Rossby (upper) wave (Figure 1.18). In the Northern Hemisphere the Rockies cause air to be pushed north – this is thought to be the reason for the position of the Rossby wave. Generally between three and six waves occur in each hemisphere and they are important in the explanation of surface depressions.

Convergence and divergence

Large-scale vertical movements of air connect upper air patterns to those at the surface. Where there is a net horizontal flow of air into a region, **convergence** is said to occur. Where there is a net outflow of air from a region, **divergence** is occurring (Figure 1.19).

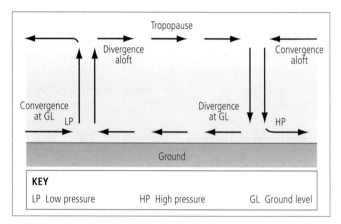

Figure 1.19 *Convergence and divergence*

The pressure gradient in a normal low pressure system sets up convergence. To maintain low pressure, air must be removed by vertical ascent, otherwise the depression fills and disappears. The vertical ascent of air is accompanied by outward divergence at high altitude. Conversely, in a high pressure system, convergence occurs at high altitude and divergence at low altitude. The change from convergence to divergence is thought to occur at an altitude where air pressure is about 600 millibars. Vertical motion is slow in relation to horizontal motion, although it can be persistent. High pressure and low pressure tend to remain stationery for a number of days.

THE GENERAL CIRCULATION

The global systems of winds or General Circulation have been summed up as the 'average of meteorological conditions' (Figure 1.17). Three major sets of wind are found in each hemisphere. The global pattern of wind movement (from high to low pressure) is mirrored by local flows of air, for example in mid-latitude depressions.

1 Trade winds blow from the north east. They cover about half of the globe from the sub-tropical high pressure (STHP) belt to the equator. There may, however, be a very

narrow belt of convergence of north westerlies at the equator (especially over the summer due to increased insolation, more so over land masses).

2 Mid-latitude westerlies are stronger in the southern hemisphere, where they are known as the Roaring Forties, because there is less friction. In the northern hemisphere they are more variable in force and direction, owing to surface irregularities and local changes of pressure.

3 Polar north easterlies are less constant in the northern hemisphere, owing to the more seasonal nature of the Arctic high pressure, compared with the permanent high pressure over Antarctica.

The surface circulation is a result of convergence and divergence. Divergence occurs at surface high pressure areas, the most important global divergence occurring at the STHP, which produces relatively calm winds, and is known as the Horse Latitudes. Weaker divergence occurs over Asia and North America during winter. Convergence occurs at the Inter Tropical Convergence Zone (ITCZ), the Equatorial Trough, and the Polar Front, between the polar easterlies and the mid-latitude westerlies.

Mechanics of circulation

The fundamental drive for the circulatory system is the imbalance of heat between the equator and the poles. In theory it should produce a 'single cell' circulation (Figure 1.20(a)), i.e. an outflow of warm air at high altitude from the equator and a return surface flow in the opposite direction. However, in the eighteenth century G. Hadley produced a three-cell model (Figure 1.20(b)). In this model, there is a low latitude cell in each hemisphere, driven by the rising of warm air at the equator, outflow aloft towards polar areas, sinking at the STHP zone and then a return towards the equator. This is a direct thermal cell, based on the temperature of the air. Another direct thermal cell exists at each pole, due to the contraction of air, initiating inflow at high level and outward divergence at low level. There is a mid-latitude cell which is maintained by the circulation of the other two and is therefore an indirect thermal cell, not based on its own temperature. Recent information has produced the Palmen model (Figure 1.20(c)), which takes into account the high altitude jet streams.

AIR MASSES

Air masses are large bodies of air whose physical properties, notably temperature and humidity, vary only slightly over a large area. Air masses derive their temperature and humidity from the regions over which they lie. These regions are known as source regions. The principal source regions are:

● areas of relative calm, such as semi-permanent, high pressure areas

● areas where the surface is relatively uniform, such as deserts, oceans and ice-fields.

The main air masses to affect the British Isles are the polar (P) and tropical (T) air masses which meet at the polar front (Figure 1.21). Some polar air masses may originate in cool temperate or sub-Arctic areas. Sometimes the British Isles is affected by equatorial and Arctic air masses. These are then generally divided into moist maritime (m) or relatively dry continental (c) depending upon the humidity characteristics of the air. (Air masses which form over oceans are moist, whereas those that form over land are relatively dry.)

Air masses move from their source regions in accordance with the General Circulation. During their migration they are modified. There are two main changes: internal modification and the effects of the surface area over which they have travelled. The modifications produce secondary air masses

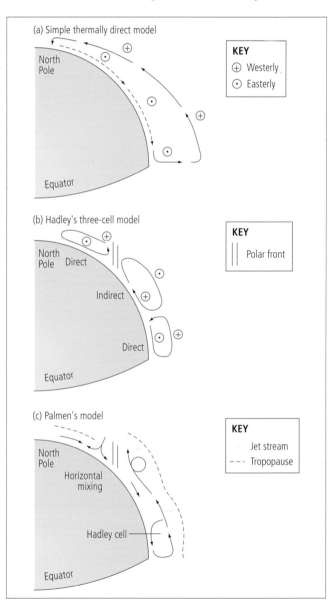

Figure 1.20 *Models of the General Circulation*

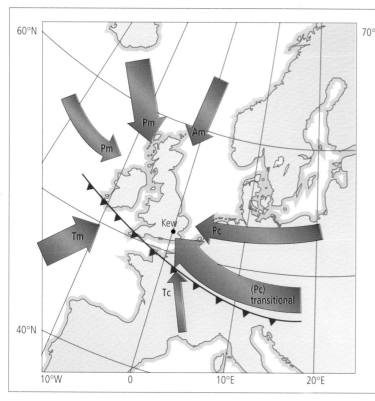

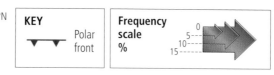

KEY ▼ ▼ Polar front

Frequency scale % 0 / 5 / 10 / 15

Polar continental (Pc) air masses originate over central Canada and Siberia, which are among the coldest places on earth. The air is cold, dry and cloud free giving extremely cold weather in the UK. In the summer months, heating at the base of the air mass makes it less stable and cloudier.

Polar maritime (Pm) air comes from the high latitudes over the Pacific and Atlantic oceans and is essentially cool, moist and relatively unstable in the lower layers. It is quite changeable, often giving sunny mornings initially, followed by clouds and/or rain.

Tropical maritime (Tm) air comes from the oceans of the lower latitudes. It is warm, moist and unstable, especially in summer when convection heating causes cooling of the air.

Tropical continental (Tc) air masses come from the hot deserts. They are hot, dry and unstable, although deficient in moisture, providing the warmest air that reaches the British Isles, for example, an 'Indian summer'.

Arctic Maritime (Am) air only affects Britain between December and February. It brings very cold clear conditions. some snow or sleet occurs in northern and easterly areas.

Figure 1.21 *Average air mass frequencies for London*
Source: Nagle, G. and Spencer, K., 1997, Advanced geography revision handbook, OUP

which are of great importance to the British Isles. For example, a migrating air mass which is warmer than the surface over which it travels is cooled, becomes more dense and therefore more stable (Figure 1.22(a)). It may form a stratiform cloud or fog but is unlikely to produce much rain. By contrast, an air mass which is originally cooler than the surface over which it passes becomes warmer, rises and thus becomes less stable (Figure 1.22(b)). The rising air is likely to produce more rain. Air which is warmed is given the suffix *w*; air which is cooled is given the suffix *k*.

FRONTAL WEATHER

When two different air masses converge they form a **front**. When Pm and Tm air masses meet, the temperature differences between them may be as much as 13°C. Such a contrast causes differences in density and allows the warm air mass to rise over the cool one. In any low pressure system or depression a number of forces operate:

- the mixing of the two air masses
- the Coriolis force
- divergence of air aloft in the upper regions of the troposphere.

The combination of these is to drag air inwards to the centre of low pressure. Warmer, lighter air invades the colder, denser air to form a warm sector, while warm air rises over the cold air at the warm front. Where the cold air pushes the warm air up a cold front is formed. The rising air is removed at higher altitudes by the jet stream.

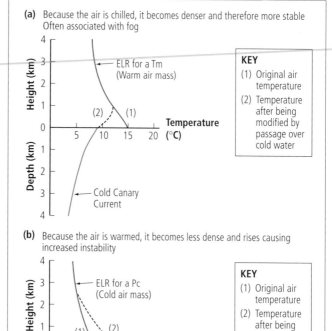

(a) Because the air is chilled, it becomes denser and therefore more stable. Often associated with fog

ELR for a Tm (Warm air mass)

KEY
(1) Original air temperature
(2) Temperature after being modified by passage over cold water

Cold Canary Current

(b) Because the air is warmed, it becomes less dense and rises causing increased instability

ELR for a Pc (Cold air mass)

KEY
(1) Original air temperature
(2) Temperature after being modified by passage over warm surface

Warm North Atlantic Drift

Figure 1.22 *Modification of lapse rates in air masses*

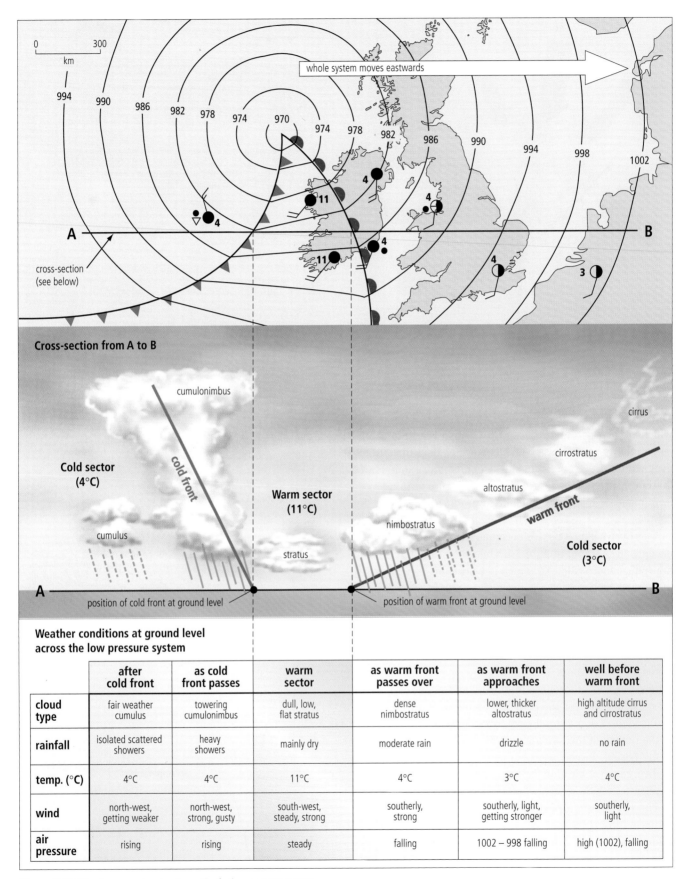

Figure 1.23 *Weather map showing the path of a low pressure system*
Source: Nagle, G. and Spencer, K., 1997, Geographical enquiries, Stanley Thornes

Weather conditions at ground level across the low pressure system

	after cold front	as cold front passes	warm sector	as warm front passes over	as warm front approaches	well before warm front
cloud type	fair weather cumulus	towering cumulonimbus	dull, low, flat stratus	dense nimbostratus	lower, thicker altostratus	high altitude cirrus and cirrostratus
rainfall	isolated scattered showers	heavy showers	mainly dry	moderate rain	drizzle	no rain
temp. (°C)	4°C	4°C	11°C	4°C	3°C	4°C
wind	north-west, getting weaker	north-west, strong, gusty	south-west, steady, strong	southerly, strong	southerly, light, getting stronger	southerly, light
air pressure	rising	rising	steady	falling	1002 – 998 falling	high (1002), falling

In general, the appearance of a warm front is heralded by high cirrus clouds (Figure 1.23). Gradually, the cloud thickens and the base of the cloud lowers. Altostratus clouds may produce some drizzle while at the warm front, nimbostratus clouds produce rain. A number of changes occur at the warm front. Winds reach a peak, are gusty and change direction; temperatures suddenly rise; pressure which had been falling remains more constant. By contrast, the cold front is marked by: a decrease in temperature; cumulonimbus clouds, heavy rain, increased wind speeds and gusting, a further change in wind direction, and a gradual increase in pressure. After the cold front has passed, the clouds begin to break up, and sunny periods are more frequent, although there may be isolated scattered showers associated with unstable polar maritime air.

The weather in a depression depends on the air masses involved. The greater the temperature difference between the air masses, the more severe the weather. Depressions are divided into two main types **ana** and **kata depressions** depending upon the vigour of the uplift of warm air. Ana fronts are formed when there is a great difference in the air masses involved, making uplift more vigorous. Kata depressions are formed when the two air masses are fairly similar in temperature so there is not much difference in density and the uplift is less intense. For a full discussion of storms, gales, hurricanes and typhoons see *Hazards* in this series.

THE EFFECT OF RELIEF

Temperature and pressure decrease as altitude increases (Figure 1.3(e)), see page 6. Aspect is also important – **adret slopes** (slopes which catch the sun) receive more insolation and are thus warmer (Figure 1.3(f)). Contrasts in temperature are more marked in mountainous areas due to the higher intensity of insolation in the thinner atmosphere as well as a more marked effect of slope angle.

Relief affects rainfall. In general, windward slopes exert an orographic effect and cause rain, even for fairly stable air. For unstable air it causes heavy rainfall. On the lee side of a slope air is descending and drier. There may even be a deficit of rain or at least a distinct rain shadow effect. This does not apply so readily to snow, since a considerable amount may be blown over the hill crests to accumulate on the lee side.

Relief also affects air flow. Any object interferes with air flow, the amount of interruption depending on wind speed and the size and shape of the object. A Föhn-type wind, a warm dry wind on the lee side of the mountain, is a noticeable example of this effect. Banner and wave clouds are also caused by mountains and hills.

Mountains may also produce their own daytime and night-time winds. An **anabatic wind** is a local wind which flows up-valley during the afternoon, especially in the summer (Figure 1.24, see page 22). Air on the mountain side is

Skills:
Planning an essay

Before you write an essay there are a number of key things that you need to do:
- read the question carefully
- read it again
- highlight or underline the key words and command words
- think about the essay structure
- plan the essay
- make sure that it is all relevant
- use key words/geographic terms.

Essay title:
Describe the major features of a temperate depression and explain the weather associated with the passage of a depression over the British Isles.

There are at least three parts to this question:
1 describe the major features of a depression
2 describe the weather associated with a depression
3 explain the weather associated with a depression.

The plan
1 Major features (could be done as a spider diagram):
- low pressure; converging air; ascending air; warm front; warm sector; cold front.
2 Weather associated with key parts of the depression:
- in front of the warm front; at the warm front, during the warm sector, at the cold front, after the cold front
- give details about temperature, pressure, wind speed, wind direction, rainfall, cloud cover.
3 Explanation will include:
- nature and type of air masses involved (a contrast in temperatures is the basic cause of a depression)
- uplift of warm air over cold air causing condensation and rainfall (ana fronts and kata fronts)
- the importance of jet streams – convergence at ground level and divergence at high level
- ana and kata depressions.

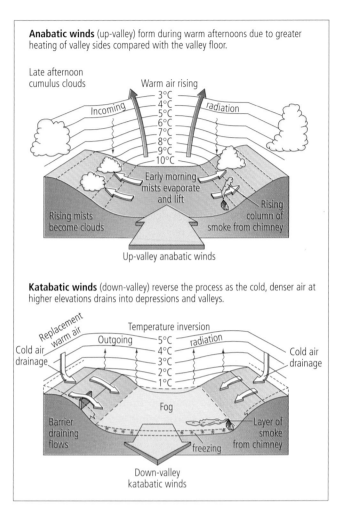

Anabatic winds (up-valley) form during warm afternoons due to greater heating of valley sides compared with the valley floor.

Katabatic winds (down-valley) reverse the process as the cold, denser air at higher elevations drains into depressions and valleys.

Figure 1.24 Anabatic and katabatic winds
Source: Nagle, G. and Spencer, K., 1997, Advanced geography revision handbook, OUP

heated by conduction to a higher temperature than air at the same level above a valley floor. This causes convectional rising above the mountain side and air moves up from the valley to take its place.

By contrast, a **katabatic wind** is a cold wind which flows downhill. These winds frequently occur at night in the valleys and are caused by the gravity flow of dense air chilled by radiation on the upper slopes. The accumulation of chilled air may cause severe frosts and frost hollows which are hazardous to agriculture. Even small frost hollows can cause problems for such activities as viticulture (wine growing) and market gardening.

Thus there are distinct mountain climates which do not belong to a major climatic belt. The effect of the increase in altitude is similar to the effect of the increase in latitude. If the mountain range is extensive, it can have a considerable effect on climate. Even individual hills or mountains can have a great effect in drier regions.

BRITAIN'S CHANGING CLIMATE

Human activities are having an increasing influence on the global climate. Between 1985–1994 the temperature on average has been about 0.2°C warmer than 1961–1990, and during the 1985–1995 decade the average global atmospheric CO_2 concentration rose by about 5%.

The likely impacts of climate change on the UK for the 2020s are:

- temperatures are expected to increase at a rate of about 0.2°C per decade, with higher rates of increase in the south east, especially in the summer; it will be about 0.9°C warmer than the average of 1961–1990 by the 2020s and about 1.6°C warmer by the 2050s
- this temperature change is approximately equivalent to a 200-kilometre northward shift of the UK climate along a south-east to north-west gradient, i.e. the difference in current temperatures between Oxford and Manchester
- annual precipitation over the UK as a whole is expected to increase by about 5% by the 2020s and by nearly 10% by the 2050s; winter precipitation will increase over the north and west, but decrease over the south and east

Positive effects

- an increase in timber yields (up to 25% by 2050s) especially the north of Britain (with perhaps some decrease in the south)
- a northward shift of farming zones by about 200–300 kilometres per degree centigrade of warming, or 50–80 kilometres per decade – this will improve some forms of agriculture, especially pastoral farming in the north-western part of Britain
- enhanced potential for tourism and recreation as a result of increased temperatures and reduced precipitation in the summer, especially in southern Britain

Negative effects

- increased soil droughtiness, soil erosion and the shrinkage of clay soils, especially in the south east
- decreased crop yields in the south east of Britain
- increased river flow in the winter and a decrease in the summer, especially in the south
- increased public and agricultural demand for water
- increased animal species, especially insects, as a result of northward migration from the continent
- decreased number of plant species due to the loss of northern and montane (mountain) types of habitat
- increased damage from storms, flooding and erosion on natural and human resources and human resource assets in coastal areas
- increased incidence of certain infectious diseases in humans and of health problems resulting from episodes of extreme temperature

Figure 1.25 The likely impact of changing climate on Britain
Source: Department of the Environment, 1996, Review of the potential effect of climate change in the UK, HMSO

0.5°C increase	1°C increase	1.5°C increase
Summer and winter precipitation increases in the north-west by 2–3%, summer precipitation decreases in the south-east by 2–3%	Summer and winter precipitation increases in the north-west by 4%, summer precipitation decreases in the south-east by 5%	Summer and winter precipitation increases in the north-west by 7%, summer precipitation decreases in the south-east by 7–8%
Annual run-off in southern Britain decreases by 5%	Annual run-off in the southern UK decreases by 10%	Annual run-off in southern Britain decreases by 15%
Frequency of the 1995 type summer (drought) increases from 1:90 to 1:25	Frequency of 1995 type summer increases from 1:90 to 1:10	Frequency of 1995 type summer increases from 1:90 to 1:3
Disappearance from the British Isles of a few niche species, for example, alpine wood fern, oak fern	Disappearance of certain species, for example ptarmigan, mountain hare	Disappearance of several species, for example red grouse
In-migration of some continental species and expansion of some species, for example, red admiral and painted lady butterflies, Dartford Warbler	Expansion of range of most butterflies, moths and birds such as golden eye and redwing	In-migration of several species, for example red-backed shrike, bee eater
Increase in overall UK timber productivity by 3%	Increase in overall UK timber productivity by 7%	Increase in overall UK timber productivity by 15%
Increase in demand for irrigation water by 21% over the increase without climate change, and in domestic demand by an additional 2%	Increase in demand for irrigation water by 42% over the increase without climate change, and in domestic demand by an additional 5%	Increase in demand for irrigation water by 63% over the increase without climate change, and in domestic demand by an additional 7%
Heating demand decreases by 6%	Heating demand decreases by 11%	Heating demand decreases by 16%

Figure 1.26 *Three scenarios for climatic change in the UK*
Source: Department of the Environment, 1996, Review of the potential effect of climate change in the UK, HMSO

• the contrast in the UK's climate is likely to become exaggerated, for example the currently dry south east will tend to become drier and the moist north west will get wetter; drought in the south east and flooding in the north west will both become more common

• sea level is expected to rise at a rate of about five centimetres per decade; the effect is likely to be greater in southern and eastern England where the land is sinking, whereas in the north it will be offset by the rising of the land which is occurring as a result of glacial unloading.

By the 2050s, the UK climate will be about 1.6°C warmer and 8% wetter than the period 1961–1990 (Figures 1.25 and 1.26). Average sea levels will be about thirty-five centimetres higher than 1961–1990 and the probability of storm surges will have increased. By 2050 the UK will be subjected to more intense rainfall events and extreme wind speeds, especially in the north. Gale frequencies will increase by about 30%.

QUESTIONS

1 How does the impact of climate change vary from the south-east of the UK to the north-west?

2 What will be the effect of **(i)** drought in summer, **(ii)** flooding in the north-west and **(iii)** demand for water?

3 Why will timber productivity increase?

URBAN CLIMATES

Cities are often warmer than the surrounding countryside areas due to higher rates of absorption of heat by concentrations of buildings – bricks and concrete absorb heat by day, store it and release it by night. This effect is increased by tall buildings and dark-coloured buildings (Figure 1.27(a), see page 24). Heat is also given off by cars, factories, industries, shops, offices and homes. The 24-hour city gives off heat day and night.

The **urban heat island** is the term given to describe the typical pattern of temperatures in and around an urban area and its surrounding countryside. Maximum temperatures are found, in general, where building densities are highest. Significant minor peaks of temperature may be located close to areas of manufacturing industry and energy production. The rest of the suburban area shows a lower temperature, although still higher than the surrounding countryside (Figure 1.28, see page 25).

The nature of heat islands may be changing. Recent research on London's heat island suggests that high levels of air pollution are decreasing the temperature by day. However, by night, the same pollution is trapping heat within the urban area. Thus, urban-rural differences may be decreasing by day but increasing by night.

The effects of urban development on precipitation have been difficult to determine, although some patterns can be

(a) The effect of city morphology on radiation received at the surface

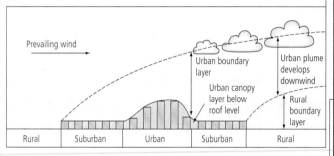

Isolated buildings

Isolated building

Sunny side heated by insolation, reflected insolation, radiation, and conduction

Heat stored and re-radiated

Shaded side

High buildings

Very little radiation reaches street level. Radiation reflected off lower walls after reflection from near tops of buildings

Low buildings

Street collects reflected radiation

(b) The structure of the urban climatic dome

Prevailing wind

Urban boundary layer

Urban plume develops downwind

Urban canopy layer below roof level

Rural boundary layer

Rural | Suburban | Urban | Suburban | Rural

(c) The morphology of the urban heat island

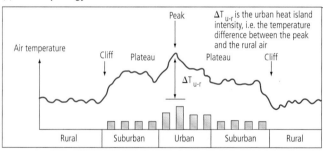

ΔT_{u-r} is the urban heat island intensity, i.e. the temperature difference between the peak and the rural air

Peak

Air temperature

Cliff | Plateau | Plateau | Cliff

ΔT_{u-r}

Rural | Suburban | Urban | Suburban | Rural

(d) Airflow modified by a single building

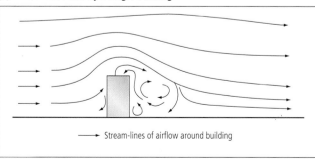

Stream-lines of airflow around building

Resultant processes

Radiation and sunshine
Greater scattering of shorter-wave radiation by dust, but much higher absorption of longer waves owing to surfaces and CO_2. Hence more diffuse sky radiation with considerable local contrasts owing to variable screening by tall buildings in shaded narrow streets. Reduced visibility arising from industrial haze.

Clouds and fogs
Higher incidence of thicker cloud cover in summer and radiation fog or smog in winter because of increased convection and air pollution respectively.
Concentrations of hygroscopic particles accelerate the onset of condensation (see Humidity below).

Temperatures
Stronger heat energy retention and release, including fuel combustion, gives significant temperature increases from suburbs into the centre of built-up areas creating heat 'islands'. These can be up to 8°C warmer during winter nights. Heating from below increases air mass instability overhead, notably during summer afternoons and evenings. Big local contrasts between sunny and shaded surfaces, especially in the spring.

Pressure and winds
Severe gusting and turbulence around tall buildings causing strong local pressure gradients from windward to leeward walls. Deep narrow streets much calmer unless aligned with prevailing winds to funnel flows along them.

Humidity
Decreases in relative humidity occur in inner cities owing to lack of available moisture and higher temperatures there. Partly countered in very cold stable conditions by early onset of condensation in low-lying districts and industrial zones (see Clouds and fogs above).

Precipitation
Perceptibly more intense storms, particularly during hot summer evenings and nights owing to greater instability and stronger convection above built-up areas. Probably higher incidence of thunder in appropriate locations. Less snowfall and briefer covers even when uncleared.

Figure 1.27 *Features of an urban microclimate*
Source: Nagle, G. and Spencer, K., 1997, *Advanced geography revision handbook*, OUP

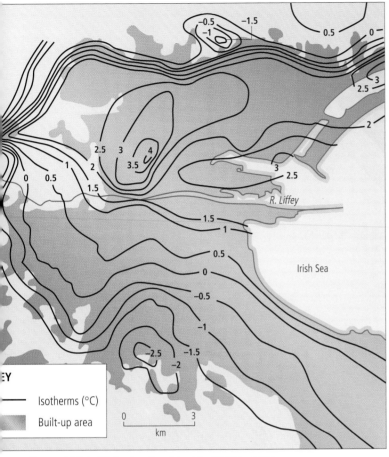

Figure 1.28 *Dublin's urban heat island for 20.00 to 1.00 hours*
Source: Drew, D.,1984, Man-environment processes, Unwin

Isotherms (°C)

Built-up area

0   3
km

Factor		Comparison with rural environments
Radiation:	global	2–10% less
	ultraviolet, winter	30% less
	ultraviolet, summer	5% less
	sunshine duration	5–15% less
Temperature:	annual mean	1°C more
	sunshine days	2–6°C more
	greatest difference at night	11°C more
	winter maximum	1.5°C more
	frost-free season	2–3 weeks more
Wind speed:	annual mean	10–20% less
	gusts	10–20% less
	calms	5–20% more
Relative humidity:	winter	2% less
	summer	8–10% less
Precipitation:	total	5–30% more
	number of rain days	10% more
	snow days	14% less
Cloudiness:	cover	5–10% more
	fog, winter	100% more
	fog, summer	30% more
	condensation nuclei	10 times more
	gases	5–25 times more

Figure 1.29 *Average changes in climate caused by urbanisation*
Source: Tivy, J., 1993, Biogeography, Longman

established (Figure 1.29). Thunderstorms are more common. This is partly due to warmer temperatures over urban areas and stronger convectional uplift. Precipitation levels may increase due to higher levels of pollution and the increased water holding capacity of warmer air. Snow is less common due to the higher temperatures. Relative humidity may be reduced because of the higher temperatures and the lack of moisture in urban areas (Figure 1.29).

Climatologists have been increasingly successful in demonstrating the urban effect on precipitation. This was initially shown in the early part of the twentieth century. Rochdale, for example, had significantly less rainfall on Sundays when the mills and factories were not producing smoke (condensation nuclei). The promotion of convection by the urban heat island, the burning of fossil fuels and the raised levels of condensation nuclei in and down-wind of the urban area often cause:

- more rainfall, especially in summer
- heavier and more frequent convective rain storms and thunder.

For example, the localised thunderstorm that brought 170 millimetres of rain to Hampstead, London, in August 1975 was influenced to a significant extent by the urban heat island.

Urban and industrial areas generate huge volumes of pollution. Many of the particles are hygroscopic (water attracting), hence water vapour condenses onto them. As a result, hours of sunshine are reduced in urban areas and fogs and smogs are more common. The problem of smog is discussed in detail in *Hazards*, in this series. As a result of pollution control, the amount of fog in Britain is decreasing (Figure 1.30, see page 26).

Winds are affected by the shape of buildings in urban areas as well as by the increased amount of energy available (Figure 1.32, see page 27). Turbulence is caused by the uneven nature of the urban skyline. Strong pressure gradients develop between the windward and leeward side of buildings and can lead to severe eddying of winds.

Under calm, high pressure conditions, country breezes blow from the colder rural areas to the warmer urban areas. As the warm air rises it creates a centre of low pressure in the urban area. Air blows from high pressure to low pressure areas, i.e. from the countryside to the urban area. Winds converge on inner urban areas and may bring pollution from outer industrial areas or road networks.

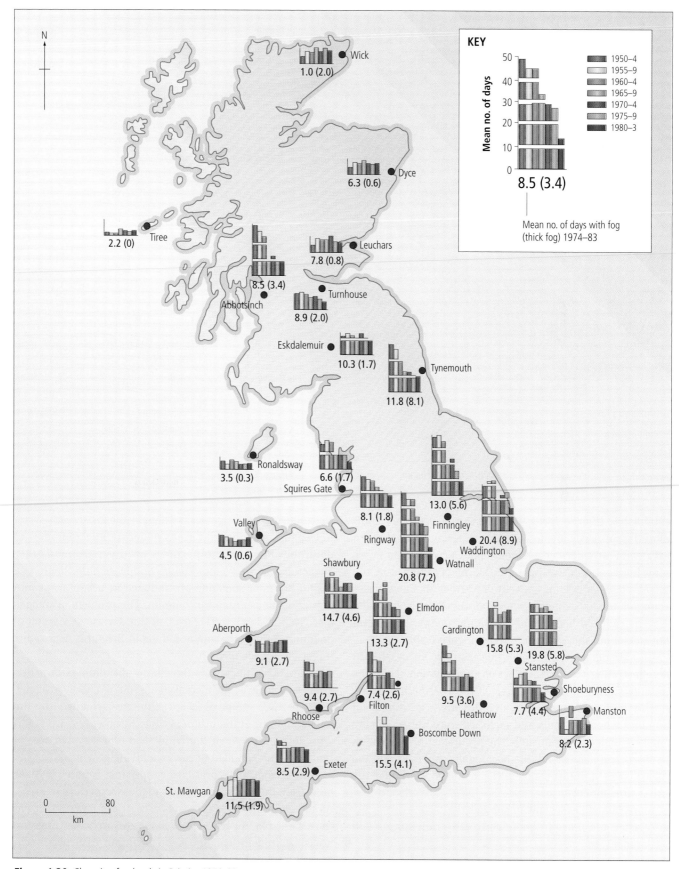

Figure 1.30 *Changing fog levels in Britain, 1950-83*

Source: Goudie, A., 1993, The human impact on the natural environment, Blackwell

Phenomenon	Consequence
Heat island	increased rainfall, increased temperature
Increased heat absorption by high walls and dark material	increased temperature
Increased surface roughness	decreased windspeed, increased eddying
Dust dome	increased fog, increased rainfall

Figure 1.31 *Effects of city surfaces on climate*
Source: Drew, D., 1984, Man-environment processes, Unwin

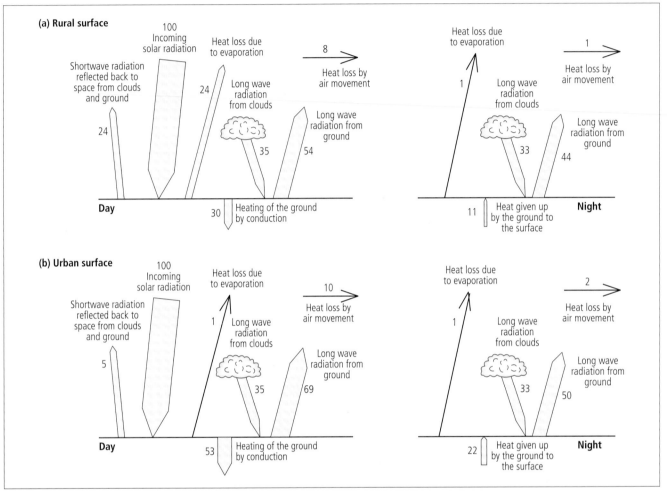

Figure 1.32 *Rural and urban energy budgets for Washington D.C. (USA) during daytime and night-time. The figures represent the proportions of the original 100 units of incoming solar radiation dispersed in different directions*
Source: University of Oxford, 1989, Entrance examination for geography

QUESTIONS

1 Study Figure 1.32 which shows energy budgets for a rural and an urban area during the day and during the night.

a) By day:

(i) How does the amount of insolation received vary between the rural area and the urban area?

(ii) How does the amount of heat lost through evaporation vary between the two areas? Explain your answer.

(iii) Explain the difference between the two areas in short-wave radiation reflected to the atmosphere (the albedo).

(iv) What are the implications of the answers to questions **ii** and **iii** for the heating of ground by conduction?

b) By night:

(i) Compare the amount of heat given up by the ground in the rural and urban area. Suggest **two** reasons for these differences.

(i) Why is there more long-wave radiation by night

from the urban area than from the rural area?

2 Study Figure 1.30 which shows the spatial variations in fog over Britain between 1950 and 1983.

a) Describe the trend* in the incidence of fog between 1950 and 1983. How do you explain these results?

b) Describe the spatial variations in fog over Britain between 1950 and 1983. How do you explain the variations you have shown?

(* In a description discuss the maximum value, minimum value, trend and any exceptions.)

SUMMARY

The climate of a location depends upon a delicate balance between long-term, short-term, large-scale and small-scale processes and features. Subtle changes to the atmospheric composition have caused far-reaching climate changes. The example of urban climates illustrates clearly how human activities and behaviour affect our climate and, ultimately, our health and well-being. Climate is not just a physical phenomenon, but is increasingly a political battleground. (This has been explored in *Hazards* in this series.)

QUESTIONS

1 With the use of an atlas, describe and explain the variations in rainfall over the British Isles.
2 Using an atlas, explain how and why temperature varies across the British Isles.
3 With the use of examples, describe and explain the term 'urban climate'.
4 Discuss the likely impact of global warming on Britain's climate.

BIBLIOGRAPHY AND RECOMMENDED READING

Barry, R. and Chorley, R., 1989, *Atmosphere, weather and climate*, Methuen

Department of the Environment, 1996, *Review of the potential effects of climate change in the United Kingdom*, HMSO

Goudie, A., 1993, *The human impact on the natural environment*, Blackwell

Hulme, M. and Barrow, E., 1997, *Climates of the British Isles*, Routledge

Musk, L., 1988, *Weather systems*, Cambridge University Press

O Hare, G. and Sweeney, J., 1986, *The atmospheric system*, Oliver and Boyd

Riley, D. and Spolton, L., 1981, *World weather and climate*, Cambridge University Press

WEB SITES

BBC Weather Centre –
http://www.bbc.co.uk/weather/
CNN Weather pages –
http://cnn.com/WEATHER/index.html
Meteosat images from Nottingham University –
http://www.nottingham.ac.uk/pub/sat-images/meteosat.html.html
Meteorological Office Home Page –
http://www.meto.govt.uk/

Chapter 2
Human impact on hydrology and rivers in Britain

Human impact on rivers and hydrology has a long history. This is because of our need for water – for drinking, cooking, washing, farming, and in manufacturing industry. In this chapter we examine the impact of urbanisation on hydrology and we look at the way in which streams and rivers have been altered in rural areas (Figure 2.1). We also look at the restoration of rivers, and at plans to manage rivers in a sustainable way.

THE IMPORTANCE OF WATER

Fresh water is vital for life. People require water for drinking and cooking, to grow food, to run industries and to provide energy. Vast numbers of people lack clean drinking water and rudimentary sanitation services. In the absence of clean water, millions of people die every year from water related diseases such as typhoid and cholera. Many of the attempts to use water more effectively have been inadequate or misdirected. Rivers, lakes and ground water aquifers are increasingly contaminated with biological and chemical wastes. In addition, massive water developments have destroyed many of the world's most productive wetlands and other aquatic habitats (see *Development and underdevelopment* in this series).

Urbanisation, for example, has a significant effect on the functioning of the hydrological cycle. It interrupts and rearranges the inputs, storage and transfer of water. Moreover, there is a clear link between urbanisation and key problems of declining water resources, increasing pollution and increased risk of flooding.

Inset 2.1
The hydrological cycle

- **Hydrology** is the study of water.
- **Precipitation** includes all forms of rainfall, snow, frost, hail and dew. It is the conversion and transfer of moisture in the atmosphere to the land.
- **Interception** is the precipitation that is collected and stored by vegetation.
- **Overland run-off** is water that flows over the land's surface.
- **Infiltration** is water that seeps into the ground.
- **Evaporation** refers to water from the ground or a lake that changes into a gas.
- **Transpiration** is water loss from vegetation to the atmosphere.
- **Evapotranspiration** is the combined losses of transpiration and evaporation.
- **The hydrological cycle** is the movement of water between air, land and sea. It varies from place to place and over time. The hydrological cycle in the Arctic is very different from that in the Mediterranean. The hydrological cycle in winter in Britain is very different from the summer.

THE EFFECT OF URBANISATION ON HYDROLOGY

Geographers are increasingly aware of the effect of urbanisation on hydrology (Figure 2.2, see page 30). In urban areas, vegetated soils are replaced by impermeable surfaces. In the UK, impermeable surfaces typically cover 20% or more of post-war urban areas; in some urban areas, such as city centres, it can be as high as 90%. By contrast, in areas of suburban detached housing, it can be as low as 5%. This change in ground cover can lead to:

- reduced water storage on the surface and in the soil
- increased percentage of run-off
- increased velocity of overland flow
- decreased evapotranspiration because urban surfaces are usually dry
- reduced percolation to ground water because the surface is impermeable.

Figure 2.1 *The human impact on rivers and hydrology – a man-made lake*

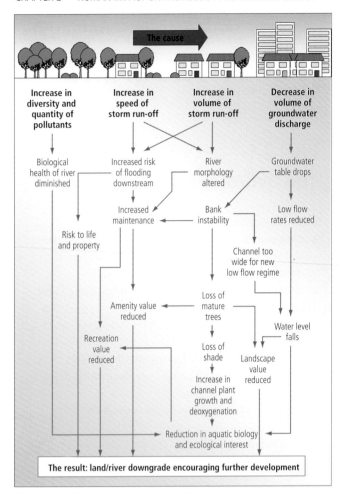

Figure 2.2 *Effects of urbanisation on hydrology*
Source: Newson, M., Catchment plans: a new geographical resource, Geography Review 9, 3, 17-24

Figure 2.3 *Urban areas affect water quality as well as quantity.*

Urbanisation also brings about major changes in the drainage density of urban areas. (Drainage density refers to the total length of stream channel per square kilometre.) The channel network is increased by stormwater sewers, gutters, gullies and drains (Figure 2.3). Prior to urbanisation, the stream channel network would have been much more limited. The increase in drainage density has a number of effects:

- it reduces the distance that overland flow has to travel before reaching the channel
- it increases the velocity of flow because sewers are smoother than natural channels
- it reduces storage in the channel system because sewers are designed to drain as completely, and as quickly, as possible.

In addition, there are rapid increases in rates of soil erosion during periods of construction (Figure 2.4). During the building of houses, roads and bridges, vegetation is cleared and this exposes the soil to storms and allows increased amounts of overland flow. Heavy machinery disturbs and churns the soil, which increases its erodibility. However, some activities may prevent erosion of the soil, by burying it under concrete, tar or tiles.

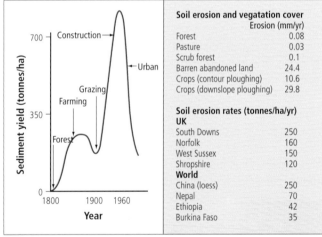

Figure 2.4 *Effect of land use on soil erosion – North America*
Source: Nagle, G, and Spencer, K., 1997, Advanced geography revision handbook, OUP

The encroachment on river channels by embankments, reclamation and by riverside roads also reduces channel width, leading to increased flood heights in the restricted channel. Bridges across the river, with bridge piers in the stream channel can restrict the free discharge of floods and so increase flood levels upstream.

The combined effects of these changes is that the flow regime, the flood hydrology, the sediment balance and the pollution load of streams are radically altered. Urbanisation increases the peak of the mean annual flood (see Inset 2.2). For example, a 243% increase resulted from the construction of Stevenage, and an 85% rise followed the building of

Skelmersdale. Likewise, the peak of the hydrograph (resulting from 25 millimetres of rainfall) grew three-fold and the lag time declined by 40%, following the paving of an extra 6% of the basin of the Silk Stream in North London. At Harlow in Essex, the paving of 15% of the clay catchment increased total run-off by almost 60 millimetres, and made it 130% of that of surrounding rural areas. River channels downstream of urban areas after the completion of building works may be enlarged as a result of floods of increased volume and reduced sediment discharges. Stevenage and Skelmersdale are just two examples.

Urban storm water passes directly to open water courses via storm sewers; foul water passes to the sewage works via separate foul sewers or old fashioned combined sewers. However, the storm water that washes off the roads and roofs of urban areas is not clean and unpolluted. Studies of urban streams show that during the start of urban run-off, the quality of water can be worse than foul sewage. Such water may contain high levels of heavy metals, volatile solids and organic chemicals. These have been found in floods of the Silk Stream, London, which is severely polluted with faecal choliform bacteria (bacteria similar to *E. coli*, which live in the gut, transmitted by faeces, through sewage). Between 20% and 40% of storm water sediments are organic in origin and most are biodegradable. By contrast, highway run-off has 5–6 times the concentration of heavy metals as roof run-off; annual run-off from one kilometre of a single carriageway of the M1 in 1984 included 1.5 tonnes of suspended sediment, 4 kilograms of lead, 126 kilograms of oil and 18 grams of hazardous polynuclear aromatic hydrocarbons.

On all urban impermeable surfaces there is initial wetting of the surface, perhaps some absorption of water by the surfaces and the filling of depressions, and evaporation from the surface into the atmosphere during and after most rainstorms. Roofs are free from the infiltration of water, but when the capacity of their gutters is exceeded in a severe storm, there is overflow on to the ground. On the other hand, it is argued that after continued heavy rainfall there is no hydrological difference between tar and saturated soil.

Figure 2.5 *Thunderstorm over an urban area*

Inset 2.2
Flood hydrographs

- A **flood**, or **storm**, **hydrograph** is a graph that shows how a storm affects a stream or river over a short period, such as a few hours or up to a few days (Figure 2.6). The graph shows a number of features which vary from stream to stream. There are a number of key terms:
- **Discharge** is the amount (volume) of water passing a point over a given length of time. This is normally measured in litres per second or cubic metres per second
- **Peak flow** marks the greatest discharge of the stream
- **Time lag** is the difference in time between the peak of the storm and the peak of the flood
- The **rising limb** is the rising floodwater, whereas the **recessional limb** is the declining floodwater
- **Base flow** is the normal flow of the river, i.e. water that passes through rocks to reach the river
- **Storm flow** or **quick flow** is the rapid flow that the storm creates. It usually flows over the surface to the stream, thus passing into the river quickly.

Beyond a certain threshold, which is hard to determine, land use has little effect on flood magnitude.

The features on a hydrograph vary with a number of factors (Figure 2.7, see page 32). For example, as gradient increases, the peak flow increases and the time lag decreases. This is because an increased gradient leads to a greater volume, and faster rates, of overland flow. Similarly, as the number of streams or channels (drainage density) in an area increases, peak flow increases and time lag decreases. This is because more water gets into streams (there are more of them) and the channels take the water rapidly away into the main river.

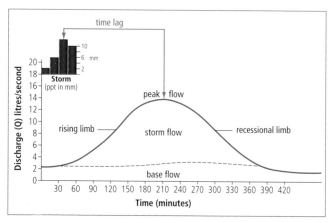

Figure 2.6 *Sherman's model storm hydrograph*
Source: Nagle, G. and Spencer, K., 1997, Geographical enquiries, Stanley Thornes

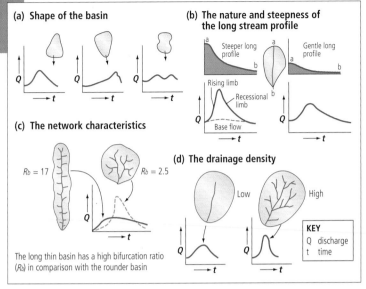

Figure 2.7 *Probable hydrograph shape in relation to some permanent characteristics of a drainage basin (Q = discharge, t = time)*
Source: Goudie, A., 1993, The nature of the environment, Blackwell

QUESTIONS

1 Study Figure 2.7. Describe and explain the effect of basin shape on a flood hydrograph.

2 a) Make a copy of Figure 2.6 and plot the figures opposite which were derived for the same storm but from a nearby urban stream.

b) What is the peak flow and time lag in the urban hydrograph?

c) How do the rising limb and recessional limbs in the new, urban hydrograph compare with the original (natural) one?

d) Explain these differences with reference to the increase in impermeable surfaces, e.g. pavements, roads, buildings, and the number of drainage channels, e.g. sewers, gutters, drains, ditches, streams.

Time (minutes)	Discharge (litres/sec)
0	4.4
30	8.0
60	20.0
90	35.0
120	44.0
150	36.0
180	26.0
210	18.5
240	14.0
270	9.5
300	7.5
330	6.5
360	6.0
390	5.5
420	4.0

Skills:
Responding to command words

When deciding how to answer a question, you need to look carefully at the 'command' words. For example, to the question: 'For a place that you have studied, **list** the factors which make it prone to flooding.' all that is required is a **list of points**, such as:

- Oxford is low lying
- two major rivers meet there
- human activity has increased the risk of flooding
- the local geology is impermeable.

By contrast, a question which says: '**Describe** the flood problem in a place that you have studied.' is looking for more **detail** and the use of **local information**. It is also asking for **full sentences**. An answer might read:

Oxford is affected by the flooding of the River Thames and the River Cherwell. The Thames floods on Port Meadow most winters and the Cherwell floods more often, as a result of human activity. The areas at risk of flooding are along the banks of both rivers. Occasional flash floods occur in the summer, but it is the frequent flooding close to the river that is the main problem in Oxford. Most of this land is now used for sports grounds, farmland and recreation.

If the question is: '**Explain** the flood problem in a place that you have studied.' the answer requires **explanation, examples** and **full sentences**. An answer might read:

Oxford suffers from many floods because two main rivers meet there. This means there is a lot of water passing through a small area. In addition, much of the area is covered by clay. Clay is an impermeable rock, which means that water does not sink into the rock but flows over the surface. Hence, in Oxford, water flows over the land and increases the risk of flooding. Also, a large part of the area is covered by concrete. Hence much of the rain flows over the surface and into the storm sewers and drains. This increases the problem of flooding.

The question: '**Evaluate** the problem of flooding in a place that you have studied.' asks us to **compare** the problem of flooding in our chosen location with other areas, and to **assess how important** flooding is. An answer might read:

Flooding in Oxford is an increasing problem. Human activity, such as the building of houses and bridges, and deforestation in agricultural areas, is increasing the amount of water that reaches the rivers. To cope with the problem, land-use zoning or management has developed. In general, land close to the rivers (i.e. the areas liable to flood) is given over to farming (Cherwell Valley), recreation (Port Meadow) and sports grounds (Magdalene College playing fields). However, compared with places such as the Ganges Delta, Oxford's flood problem is not very serious. It causes economic disruption, but it does not usually lead to a loss of life or a loss of property.

Source: based on Nagle, G., 1998, Geography through diagrams, OUP

CHANGES IN THE RURAL HYDROLOGICAL CYCLE

In the UK there have been many changes in the rural hydrological cycle due to processes such as deforestation, land use changes and mining. In addition, rivers have been straightened, widened, deepened, dammed and, in places, covered. These changes are analysed throughout this chapter. One change is in water quality.

In recent decades, the rising levels of nitrates in rivers and groundwater have had a noticeable effect upon rural hydrology. This is often referred to as **eutrophication**, the nutrient enrichment of streams, ponds and groundwater. There are three main reasons why the high concentrations of nitrogen in rivers and groundwater are a problem. First, the loss of fertiliser is an economic loss to the farmer. Second, high nitrate concentrations in drinking water may affect human health. Third, nitrogen compounds can cause undesirable effects in the aquatic ecosystems, especially excessive growth of algae.

As we saw in *Development and underdevelopment* in this series, there is a very distinct geographic pattern to the level of nitrates in the UK's water. Highest levels, over 11.3 mg/l^{-1} (milligrammes of nitrate per litre of water) are mostly found in eastern parts of England, the lowest levels, less than 2.8 mg/l^{-1}, are found in Scotland, north-west England and central Wales. In general, there is an east-west trend with higher values in the east and lower values in the west. There are, however, certain anomalies. Parts of south-east England have very low values (<2.8 mg/l^{-1}) while there are quite high rates (5.6-11.3 mg/l^{-1}) in the south-west and in parts of northwest England (see Figure 4.24, page 67 in *Development and underdevelopment* in this series). Figure 2.8 shows the nitrogen cycle for a plot on which winter wheat has been grown continuously for many years. Inputs of nitrogen from fertiliser, rainfall and biological fixation are balanced by crop uptake, denitrification and leaching. If fertiliser is applied in the spring, leaching losses are usually low. Nevertheless only about 70% of the total input of nitrogen is used by the crop.

Even when fertiliser is not applied in autumn, arable soils often contain much inorganic nitrogen. Some of this will be fertiliser unused by the previous crop, but most will come from the mineralisation of organic matter caused by autumn ploughing. Ploughing releases vast quantities of nitrogen and, unless a new crop is planted quickly, much of this will be lost by leaching. Another influence is climate. There is normally much mineralisation in the autumn when warm soils begin to become wet. As grass grows, it can absorb the nitrate produced, but with bare soil the nitrate is liable to leaching. The problem is especially severe when a dry summer is followed by a wet autumn, when much organic matter in the soil may be mineralised and leached.

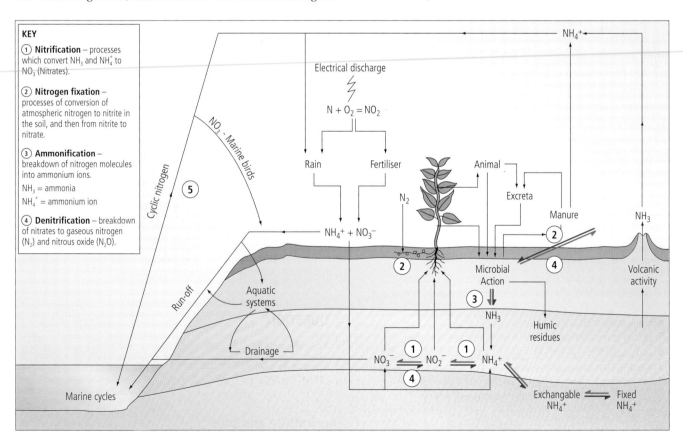

Figure 2.8 *The nitrogen cycle for a plot under continuous winter wheat receiving approximately 144 kg/ha^{-1} every year*

Source: Briggs, D., et al, 1997, *Fundamentals of the physical environment*, Routledge

Year	Slapton Wood (Devon) (Area = 1 km²)	Windrush (Gloucs.) (Area = 300 km²)	Thames at Oxford (Area = 3,400 km²)
1972	5.9	n.a.	6.5
1973	5.6	5.1	5.9
1974	5.9	6.0	6.7
1975	6.4	6.1	6.4
1976	6.9	4.5	5.4
1977	8.3	7.7	10.7
1978	7.7	7.6	7.8
1979	6.8	7.7	8.8
1980	6.9	7.3	7.4
1981	6.7	7.6	7.9
1982	7.8	7.2	7.8
1983	6.8	7.7	8.6
1984	6.9	7.3	7.9
1985	8.3	9.1	9.4
1986	9.2	8.5	7.7
1987	9.2	8.5	7.7
1988	8.8	9.0	8.0

Figure 2.9 Trends in nitrate concentrations (mg/l⁻¹) for three UK rivers, 1972–1988

Data sources: P.J. Johnes; Thames Water Authority; Slapton Ley Field Centre

Source: Burt, T. and Haycock, N., 1990, Farming and nitrate pollution, Geography, 76, 60-3

Since 1945, agriculture in the UK has become much more intensive. Considerably more fertiliser is used, fields are ploughed more frequently and more land is devoted to arable crops. In addition, grassland is farmed more intensively. Nitrogen is a key component for plant growth and so farmers are keen to apply nitrogen fertilisers. National and European policies promote agricultural self-sufficiency, and the manufacturers of nitrate fertilisers are also keen to see an increase in their use. Their use in the UK rose from just 200 000 tonnes in 1945 to a peak of about 1.6 million tonnes in the late 1980s. However, the serious ecological, economic and health effects combined with recent legislation have curtailed their use.

The increased concentrations of nitrates in rivers in the 1970s and 1980s were due to a combination of increased rainfall – the early 1970s conditions were dry; the late 1970s and early 1980s were much wetter – combined with modern agricultural practices (Figure 2.9).

The annual cost of cleaning nitrate-rich groundwater is estimated at between £50 million and £300 million. In terms of water treatment, the removal of nitrate is costly. The cheapest method of treatment is to blend high and low nitrate waters, though this can still be expensive. Storage of water in reservoirs is helpful. Good farming practices can help to reduce nitrate losses (Figure 2.10). For example, farmers should avoid autumn application of fertiliser, sow crops in autumn and avoid spreading fertiliser if heavy rain is forecast. The role of flood plains as buffer zones between farmlands and rivers is important. It suggests that strategically placed set-aside land might solve the difficulties of over production and the pollution problems associated with modern agriculture.

HYDROLOGY AND CLIMATE CHANGE

In the British Isles, the significant changes that seem to be taking place and are predicted to continue (as discussed in Chapter 1, Britain's changing climate) will have a profound effect on rivers and the hydrological cycle.

Since the late 1980s the problem of high nitrate levels in rivers has been tackled in a number of ways:

1 changing land-use; less arable land, either due to set-aside, wood lots or pastoral farming
2 changing inputs; extensification of agriculture
3 avoiding the use of nitrogen fertilisers between mid-September and mid-February when rainfall is higher
4 giving preference to winter crops
5 sowing cover crops early
6 applying fertilisers in early spring when plants need nutrients most
7 avoiding riparian (riverside) fields
8 not applying fertilisers if the weather forecast is heavy rain
9 using less nitrogen fertilisers if the previous year was dry.

Figure 2.10 Tackling the problem of high nitrate levels in rivers
Source: Nagle, G. and Spencer, K., 1996, A geography of the European Union, OUP

QUESTION

1 Study Figure 2.9.

a) Choose an appropriate method to show the data in Figure 2.9.

b) Describe the results that you have shown.

c) How do you explain the anomalies (blips) in the early 1970s?

Agriculture and soils

Limitations caused by reduced water availability in the south and east, coupled with higher temperatures and increased evapo-transpiration may shift potential production of arable and other field crops northwards and westwards as well as placing extra pressure on the supply of water for irrigation.

The soils of the southern UK are likely to be most at risk from climate change, especially from the increase in summer droughtiness which will give rise to an increased need for irrigation for agriculture. In the northern UK, the combination of higher temperatures and increased rainfall may be beneficial to the soils found there, and allow a wider range of crops to be grown. However, adverse effects on soils and increased incidence of pests, weeds and diseases could reduce or negate any yield increases attributable to climatic change.

Wetland areas of the southern UK will be at risk from drying out, and peat soils will be lost at increasing rates due to drying and wind erosion. Most of the clay soils of the southern UK will be subject to more intense shrinkage in the summer with potentially severe implications for building foundations.

It is predicted that soil erosion will increase throughout the UK. The predicted drier summers in the south would leave the lighter soils more prone to wind erosion, and wetter winters would lead to more water erosion. Higher rainfall in the north would cause increased erosion by water.

Over 50% of grade 1 agricultural land in England and Wales lies below the five metre contour, where it might be affected by any rise in sea level.

Landscape changes

The changes in plant communities, species, migrations, losses and gains will in time change many landscapes:

- montane plant communities may be lost
- heaths may become subject to more frequent fires, as southern Britain becomes warmer and experiences dry summers such as those in 1990 and 1995
- wetlands may dry out more frequently with the change in species composition, especially if current water obstruction from aquifers was increased

Inset 2.3
Flora, fauna and landscape

The natural biota of the UK has been most profoundly altered by human activities in the past, and over the next fifty years land-use changes are likely to have a greater impact. A 1°C increase in temperature may significantly alter the species composition in about half of the protected areas of the UK. Overall, the number of animal species (especially insect) in most parts of the UK is likely to increase, due to immigration and expansion of species ranges. By contrast, the number of plant species may decrease, and a substantial number of the 506 currently endangered species may be lost because species-rich native communities may be invaded by competitive species, and some wet, montane and coastal communities will be lost.

A 20–30 centimetre increase in sea level would adversely affect mud flats and some salt marshes, including important bird nature reserves. Climate change will occur too rapidly for species to adapt in an evolutionary sense. Mitigating measures that can be taken include the translocation and rescue of species, the provision of habitat corridors, fire control and control of eutrophication.

Cold-blooded vertebrates (amphibians and reptiles) may become more active and noticeable during mild winters and earlier springs, as in 1989 and 1990, but they will not necessarily become more numerous. Their populations are already limited by the availability of habitats, rather than by climate.

The main effects of the high temperatures in 1984, 1990 and 1995 were an increase in the abundance, activity and geographic spread of many insects. Some of these insects were pests, such as aphids in 1989, and wasps in 1990 and 1995.

The main species or communities that may become endangered by climate change include:

- montane/alpine and northern/arctic plant and animal species which have nowhere to go if it becomes warmer – good plant examples are the tufted saxifrage and alpine woodsia fern; animal examples include the mountain hare, ptarmigan, snow bunting and white fish
- species confined to particular locations from which they cannot readily escape because, for instance, they occupy cold, damp refuges, isolated habitats, or are dependent on particular other species for pollination, food or to complete their life cycle
- species living in salt marshes and soft coastal communities (easily eroded areas – often salt marshes/sand dunes/mudflats), that cannot retreat landward in the face of sea level rise.

- coastal dunes and rocks may be invaded more rapidly by alien species such as the hottentot fig
- salt marshes and brackish water habitats may be lost as sea level rises
- some broad leafed woodland and dry areas of Britain may decline further in response to increased frequency of summer droughts, particularly in the south, where summer droughts are forecast to be more frequent and severe.

Water resources

The sensitivity of UK industry, the water industry and water users to climatic change has been shown by the droughts of 1988–92 and 1995 (Figure 1.25, see page 22) and by the floods of 1993, 1994 and 1995. Increased winter rainfall and wetter catchment conditions are likely to increase the frequency of river flooding. However, it is not clear whether ground water recharge will increase in these wetter winters, since the recharge season could be shorter due to the increased autumn and spring evaporation.

Construction

Climate change is likely to have a great impact on building and other types of construction through higher summer temperatures, increased winter rainfall and, in the north of the UK, increased extreme winds. When sea defences are breached, the damage to construction in the affected areas will be very considerable. Soil moisture movements on shrinkable clays will increase and more careful attention to foundation design will be needed in vulnerable areas.

Recreation and tourism

Given an overall increase in tourist activity, there will be a need for improved management of visitor pressure at peak periods to maintain the quality of tourist sites. Problems with environmental protection could arise in key settings, eroding beaches and threatening moors and heaths with an increased fire risk. In the north of the UK any significant increases in rainfall, wind speed or cloud cover are likely to offset the more general advantages associated with higher temperatures. The Scottish ski industry may well decline if snow confidence becomes less secure than at present. Potential rises in sea level will adversely affect fixed waterfront facilities such as marinas and piers. On beaches backed by sea walls, increased erosion could lead to a loss of beach area.

QUESTIONS

1 How and why is Britain's climate changing?

2 What are the effects of Britain's changing climate on the natural environment?

3 Make a list to show those who are (i) likely to benefit from Britain's changing climate and (ii) those who are likely to be disadvantaged.

RIVERS

Humans have straightened river channels for navigation and flood control for many centuries. By straightening channels, the river's gradient and velocity are increased. This allows the river to erode deeper, thereby increasing its capacity to hold water. In some areas artificial channels dominate. These are characterised by a proliferation of straight water courses on a map, indicating drainage ditches.

River landforms may be changed quite considerably by modifying channels and by other human activity, such as the building of reservoirs, bridges and jetties. These may increase or decrease flow and upset the natural dynamic equilibrium of the river. Many of the changes caused by humans are accentuations or reproductions of natural processes – the result is to compress such changes in time and to intensify them in effect.

Rivers and erosion

Rivers erode in four main ways:

- **abrasion** is the wearing away of the bed and bank by the load carried by a river
- **attrition** is the wearing away of the load carried by a river, creating smaller, rounder particles
- **hydraulic action** is the force of air and water on the side of rivers and in cracks
- **solution** is the removal of chemical ions, especially calcium.

The type and amount of erosion that is carried out by a river depends upon a number of factors. For example, the heavier and sharper the **load** the greater the potential for erosion. Similarly, with increased **velocity** there is greater potential for erosion. This is especially true on steep slopes. Soft or unconsolidated **rock-types**, such as sand and gravel, are more easily eroded than hard rocks such as basalt and granite. Certain rocks such as chalk and limestones are eroded by solution (as well as abrasion and hydraulic action) when the water is acidic. Increasingly, **human impact**, such as deforestation, and the building of dams and bridges, interfere with the natural flow of a river and frequently increase the rate of erosion.

Rivers and human activity

Rivers are very attractive to people for a variety of reasons. These include:

- a source of drinking water
- a source of fertile silt for agriculture
- as a line of communication and navigation
- as a source of power
- for fishing
- for recreation.

But rivers can also cause problems. The flood hazard is extremely dangerous for people's lives and their possessions.

Many settlements are built to reduce the risk of flooding. Oxford is an excellent example. Much of the flood plain of the Thames and the Cherwell has not been built upon, but left for farming and recreational grounds. Housing and industry have tended to locate on the higher ground, free from flooding.

People have tried to reduce the effects of flooding by:
- reinforcing river banks with steel, concrete and wood
- diverting streams and creating new flood relief channels
- raising the banks of the river.

(These activities are discussed in detail in *Hazards* in this series.)

Rivers are also affected by the building of dams, such as the Kielder Dam in Northumberland. The effect of dams is to:
- reduce the speed of water flow
- control the amount of water in a river
- cause deposition behind the dam
- increase erosion below the dam ('clear water erosion')
- change ecosystems
- increase pressure on rocks and cause earthquakes.

Dams provide:
- reliable water throughout the year
- navigation
- hydroelectric power
- water for irrigation
- safety from flooding.

Case study:
The lost rivers of London

There are very few rivers in London, other than the Thames. Many streams, such as the Wandle and the Fleet, have been built over. This is mainly because they were 'in the way' of human activity. As London developed, many of its rivers became extremely polluted. They served little function other than a way of transporting unwanted material. Hence, town planners were only too happy to build over them.

Figure 2.11 *The rivers of London*
Source: *Geographical magazine, The lost rivers of London, Jan. 1994*

The earliest accounts of London date from 1180. These speak of the area north of the river as 'fields for pasture, and a delightful plain of meadowland, interspersed with flowing streams, on which stand mills, whose clack is very pleasing to the ear. Close by lies an immense forest in which are densely wooded thickets, the coverts of game, stags, fallow deer and wild boars.'

To the north of the River Thames is the higher land of Hampstead and Highgate rising to about 125 metres and sending out spurs in all directions. On the south side of the Thames there is a long ridge running from west to east, crossed at various intervals by a number of valleys.

The rivers of London (Figure 2.11, see page 37) had many uses. They provided power (there were over thirty mills on the River Wandle), drinking water, fishing and shipping routes. So what happened? The decline of the River Fleet has been described as a decline from a river to a brook, to a ditch, to a drain. It suffered because there wasn't enough demand for a river or a canal but too much demand for a street, and so it was covered over and now acts mainly as a sewer/drain. Of all London's rivers, only the River Wandle (Figure 2.12), which runs north through Morden, Merton and Wandsworth to the River Thames, has been relatively untouched and maintains its course to the River Thames without too much hindrance (Figure 2.13).

However, the River Wandle is affected by high levels of pollution. For example, near Beddington, south of Mitcham, local residents claim that on most Fridays there is an increase in the amount of oil in the river as garage mechanics clear up for the weekend.

The lost rivers are not completely lost from the landscape. Roads, for example, often follow the course of rivers; Faringdon Street follows the lower parts of the Fleet (Figure 2.14, see page 40), and railways, which must avoid steep gradients, also follow the rivers. The Liverpool Street railway line leaves London along the Lea Valley; the Kings Cross line passes between the higher ground of Highbury and Tufnell Park; the name 'Marylebone' is a simplified version of St Mary by the Bourne (a bourne is a winter stream). Almost all of the lost rivers of London form some sort of boundary, for example, the Westbourne is part of the boundary of the City of Westminster.

Despite the fact that they have been constrained and abused by industries, planners and engineers, the rivers still create problems, such as flooding, pollution, disease and bad smells. However, there are plans to restore some of London's rivers. The Effra Redevelopment Agency is campaigning to bring back the River Effra for the enjoyment of locals and there are plans to use the Wandle to generate power again.

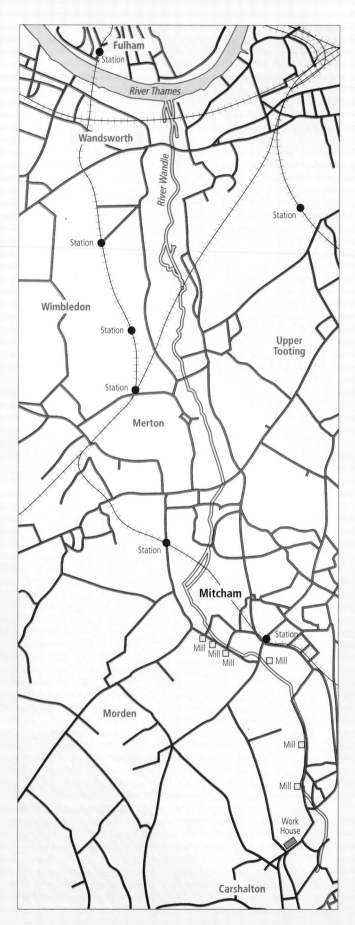

Figure 2.12 *The course of the River Wandle in 1891.*

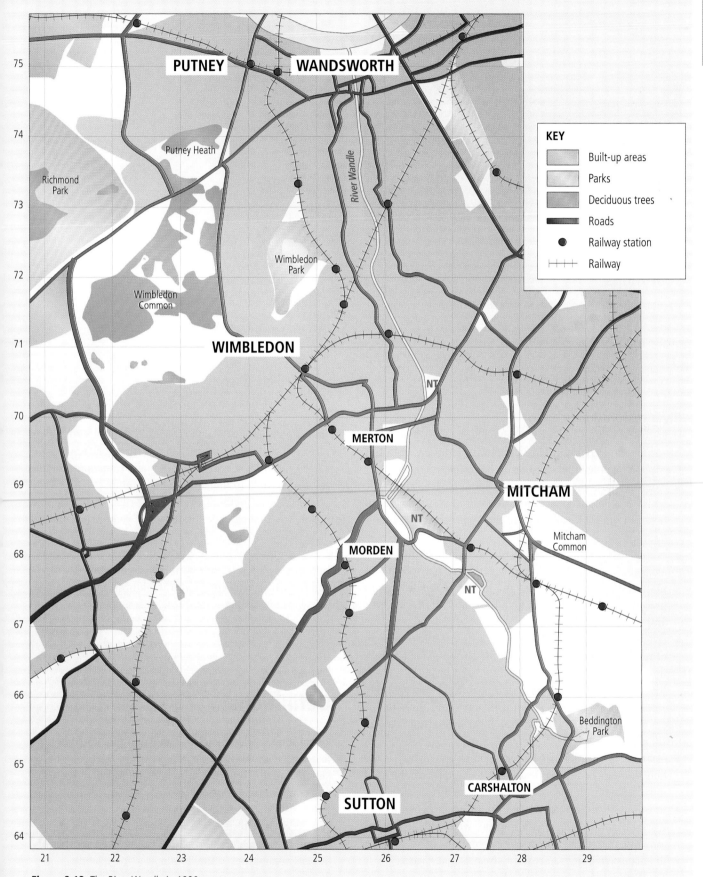

Figure 2.13 The River Wandle in 1990

Figure 2.14 *The River Wandle – an urban stream*

Figure 2.15 *All that remains of the River Fleet – New Bridge Street*

QUESTIONS

1 Study Figures 2.12 and 2.13 which show the River Wandle and its catchment in 1891 and in 1990.

a) In what ways has the catchment changed since 1891?

b) Approximately how much of the catchment was covered by buildings in 1891 and in 1990?

c) What happens to the River Wandle at GR 265698 and GR 259726. See also Figure 2.14.

d) Describe in detail the course of the Wandle from its source in squares 2764 and 2864 to its confluence with the River Thames in square 2575.

River restoration

Over the last fifty years rivers have been seriously affected by urban and agricultural flood defences, land drainage and floodplain urbanisation. The result has been:

- extensive straightening and deepening of river channels, which has damaged wildlife habitats, reduced the value of fisheries and reduced much of the natural appeal of river landscapes
- major loss of floodplains and wetlands to intensive agriculture and urbanisation, which has destroyed floodplain habitats and reduced the ability of floodplains to provide economically valuable functions, such as water and sediment storage
- rivers being used intensively as transport routes, carriers of waste disposal, for industrial purposes, water abstraction and recreation.

River restoration schemes are becoming increasingly common as the benefits of natural rivers and their floodplains are realised. The aims of the River Restoration Project (RRP) are to:

- establish international demonstration projects which show how the state-of-the-art restoration techniques can be used to recreate natural ecosystems in damaged river corridors
- to improve understanding of the effects of restoration work on nature conservation value, water quality, visual amenity, recreation and public perception
- to encourage others to restore streams and rivers.

The RRP is an independent organisation backed by scientific and technical advisers drawn mainly from organisations connected with rivers and river environments. Its aims are to restore and enhance damaged rivers for conservation, recreation and economic use, returning them as closely as possible to their natural condition.

There are two methods of restoring rivers – natural and artificial. The first can take hundreds of years, consequently artificial restoration is often the chosen method. The benefits are greatest when natural channel forms, flows, sediment loads and floodplains are reinstated. However, structures which only copy natural features, such as a weir, give fewer benefits than natural features.

Inset 2.4
Definitions

Restoration – A complete structural and functional return to a river's natural state

Rehabilitation – A partial structural and functional return to a river's natural state

In practice most restoration schemes will only partially restore or rehabilitate a river, due to the large number of human-related uses in the floodplains, for example, buildings, farmland, transport.

Case study:
Improving the River Cole

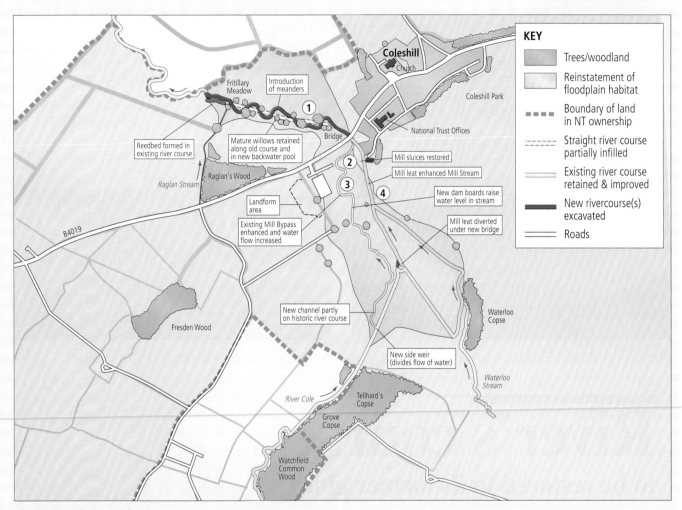

Figure 2.16 *The River Cole project*
Source: Riverside Restoration Project

The River Cole, near Swindon, is one of three river restoration sites financially supported by LIFE, a European Union (EU) organisation which provides grant aid for schemes of environmental benefit (Figure 2.16). The others are the River Skerne in Darlington and the River Brede in Denmark. The aim of the RRP for the River Cole is to change the water course, improve water quality and manage the bankside vegetation. The project is being run by the RRP, the Environment Agency (formerly the National Rivers Authority), English Nature, the National Trust, the Countryside Commission, the Department of Agriculture for Northern Ireland and the EU.

- **Stretch 1** – It is planned to raise the river bed below Coleshill Bridge to bring it back in line with its floodplain and to make it an important feature in the local landscape. This involves the introduction of more gravel riffles (fast flowing midstream ridges) and some small weirs (Figure 2.17, see page 42).

- **Stretch 2** – The new river bed will run at the higher level along this stretch to fit in with the mill channel just upstream of the bridge. Rather than filling in part of the straightened river, a new meandering course will be cut (Figure 2.18, see page 42). Parts of the old course can then be retained as backwaters which will provide shelter for fish, birds and insects during high flows. This also means that neighbouring fields will flood more frequently, which will help to recreate a water meadow.

- **Stretch 3** – The restoration of the ancient course of the Cole appears to be possible at this site. Floodwaters will restore the flood meadows along the western side of the mill.

- **Stretch 4** – The RRP hopes to restore the Cole mill for occasional operation. The water levels in the Mill Stream need to be raised for this to happen. This feeder stream (known locally as the 'leat') is to be developed as a long lake with wet pasture and reed beds along its side. (Reed, willow and alder tree beds cleanse streams which have been polluted by silt, fertiliser and treated sewage. A few carefully located beds of these plants are very effective at removing unwanted debris and pollutants.)

The overall aim of the proposals is to increase the extent to which the river and its floodplain interact, to sustain a landscape that is rich in riverine and wetland wildlife. The key to success is the management of the floodplain, worked out in conjunction with local land managers. The main road (B4019) at Coleshill Bridge, and nearby buildings and sports fields, have been protected from the increased risk of erosion and flooding.

Figure 2.17 *River Cole – riffle*

Figure 2.18 *River Cole – new meandering course*

River's course
to be restored to its former glory

Thousands of tons of soil are being moved as the River Cole's natural meandering course is restored after centuries of human tampering.

The work at Coleshill, near Faringdon, is being done by the River Restoration Project, a non-profit making association of representatives from the National Rivers Authority, National Trust, English Nature and the Countryside Commission.

Coordinator Martin Janes said, 'Milling has been carried out along the river for about a thousand years but serious changes occurred about 300 years ago, when the river started to be diverted, deepened and straightened to power mills and drain farmland.'

The 1.25 mile stretch of river will have parts of its bed raised with the introduction of weirs.

Low ground will be flooded to coax new wildlife into the area. Fish will also benefit from spawning in sheltered new backwater habitats.

The project aims to encourage the return of redshanks, snipe and reed warblers.

Conservation campaigner Mr. David Bellamy said, 'This is the best news I have heard about rivers for years. The group has the vision and know-how to make this exciting project work.'

Monitoring of the area includes checking water flow and quality, fish and other wildlife in the river, plants in the water and floodplain, the bird population, changes to the landscape, and the involvement and reaction of local people to the project's effects.

The work being carried out at Coleshill will also be used to gauge the damage caused by industrial development and prove the benefits of improving Britain's waterways.

Figure 2.19
Source: *The Daily Telegraph, October 1996*

Figure 2.20
Source: *The Oxford Times, August 1995*

The River Cole is alive with dace and snipe after a £500 000 project to restore meanders, pools and wet meadows destroyed by 1970s drainage schemes.

The River Restoration Project intends to show the benefits of allowing silts carried by winter floods to fertilise the wet meadows and prevent flooding lower down.

On the Cole, most of the river has been diverted down its old, meandering course.

A 24-acre wet meadow has been created out of an arable field and it is hoped to recolonise this with snake's head fritillaries from a fragment of water meadow nearby.

Inset 2.5
Benefits of restoration

- Nature conservation: wetland wildlife in the river and on the floodplain
- Fisheries: species diversity and numbers
- Water quality: increased interception of pollutants by vegetation and natural settling of sediments on flood plain and river bed
- Flood defence: additional flood storage is offered by the enlarged floodplain
- Recreation: there is a strong public perception in favour of natural landscapes

The River Skerne, Darlington

The River Skerne shares many characteristics with other urban streams:

- it has a high sediment load, especially of silt
- it is slow moving
- banks are overgrown with weeds
- many polluting activities, such as factories and sewage works discharge into the river
- the floodplain contains a large amount of housing, roads, railways and industrial development.

The aim of the Skerne restoration project is to improve the quality of the river without reducing its function for flood defence (Figure 2.21). In particular, the Skerne will be improved by:

- the creation of new meanders in the river
- the introduction of sloping, rather than vertical, banks
- the growth of wetland plant species on the inside of meander belts
- strengthening the banks by planting trees and reeds
- creation of new wetland ecosystems
- improving the water quality from the sewage works
- creating a new footbridge so that access to the site is improved
- planting native species of plants to attract a richer, more diverse insect population.

Rivers and their floodplains are complex physical systems. However, they also have economic, social and political consequences. Balancing the physical demands of rivers with the economic and political demands based on the human use of the floodplain is difficult. The impact of human activity on natural systems is often negative but the late 1990s may, perhaps, be seen as the dawn of a new era in which human efforts are directed at trying to restore rivers to their natural state rather than continually try to use and abuse them.

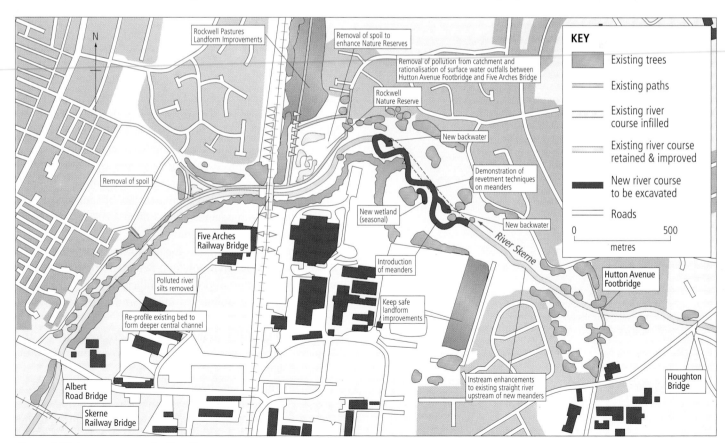

Figure 2.21 *Improvements to the River Skerne*
Source: Riverside Restoration Project

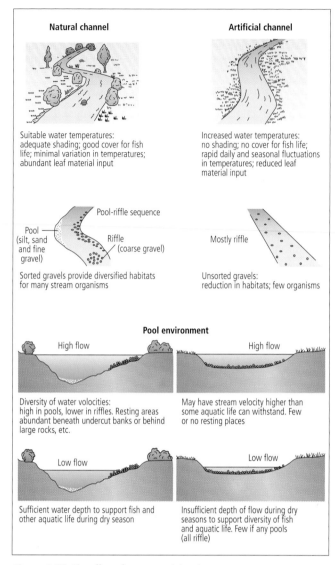

Figure 2.22 *The effect of stream straightening*
Source: Goudie, A., 1993, The human impact on the natural environment, Blackwell

QUESTIONS

1 Study Figures 2.16 and 2.22. State **three** ways in which the restored River Cole differs from the Mill Stream.

2 Study Figure 2.22 which shows the effect of straightening the stream channel. Answer the following questions.

a) Why does the temperature of the straightened stream increase?

b) Why does the velocity of the straightened stream increase?

c) Why are there fewer plants and animal species in the straightened stream?

3 What do you think is meant by the following terms: **(i)** the water table, **(ii)** a water meadow, **(iii)** a fritillary meadow ?

4 How does the land use of the River Cole catchment area (Figure 2.16) differ from that of the River Wandle (Figure 2.13)?

5 How can the restoration of the River Cole be used 'to gauge the damage caused by industrial development and prove the benefit of improving Britain's waterways'? In what ways can it help to show this?

MANAGING RIVERS

The Environment Agency (EA) has a duty to conserve and enhance the environment when carrying out any of its functions, and a further duty to promote conservation and enhancement more widely. For water resources, this includes overall policies on water quality and surface water management, flood management, mineral extraction, sewage capacity, water efficiency and demand, waste disposal, habitat enhancement and restoration, and research and development. For example, in the Thames region there is a need for more new housing, for the development of derelict sites, for mineral extraction, flood defences, a supply of safe drinking water and sustained agricultural yields. To help achieve these goals, the National Rivers Authority (NRA), (later to become the Environment Agency), developed the idea of **catchment management planning**.

Catchment management plans

Catchment management plans are plans for the integrated planning, management and development of the water environment and identification of appropriate levels for growth in the river catchment. Catchment management planning requires a Catchment Management Plan (CMP) to be drawn up for each natural river catchment throughout England and Wales. The CMP entails data evaluation, issues analysis, external liaison and consultation, and provides a vehicle to focus attention on the water environment. By their very nature, CMPs involve close contact with local communities and other interested organisations.

The first practical application was for the Cotswold Water Park in the Upper Thames CMP in 1996 (Figure 2.23). The first CMPs were drawn up in the early 1990s and are planned for completion by the end of 1998. CMPs can only be achieved through a partnership between a number of key agencies and organisations, such as town and country planners, local authorities, environmental groups and land owners; CMPs are funded from a variety of sources.

Catchment Management Plans have already achieved a number of objectives, including:

- an outline of future plans for each catchment, allowing it to reach its full environmental potential (Figure 2.24)
- the identification of possible conflicts of interest, such as between flood defence systems and preserving river ecosystems
- bringing together different interest groups, such as the private water companies and environmentalists and industrialists.

Catchment Management Plans vary significantly. Each is site-specific but all share a common purpose of trying to control inappropriate land use and encourage better water management practices. Some plans have been developed for small catchments (such as the Wandle, see page 37),

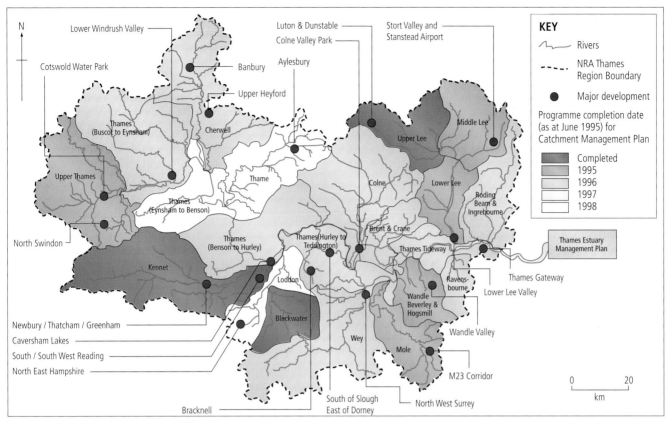

Figure 2.23 *Major development locations and catchment plans*
Source: Thames Water, 1995, Thames 2000, National Rivers Authority

Figure 2.24 *Water related assets in the River Thames catchment, showing the mismatch between environmentally sensitive areas and urban growth*
Source: Thames Water, 1995, Thames 2000, National Rivers Authority

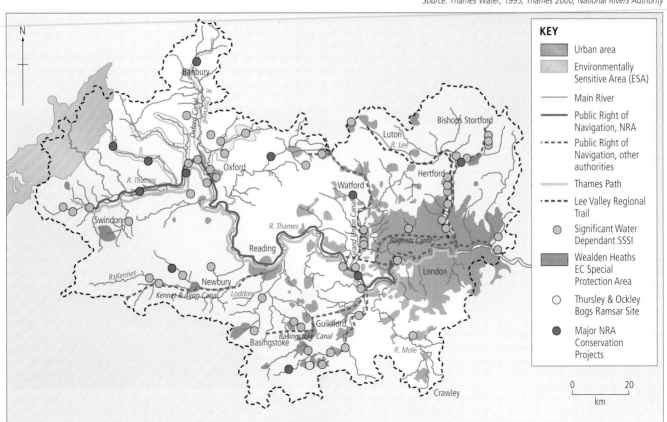

while others deal with much larger catchments (such as the Thames). Each plan identifies the main issues and suggests how they should be tackled.

Agenda 21

The United Nations Conference on Environment and Development (1992) resulted in Agenda 21 schemes. Agenda 21 plans are drawn up by local councils to achieve sustainable development (Figure 2.25). The links between Agenda 21 and Catchment Management Plans are strong. Agenda 21 allows for:

- increased emphasis on environmental considerations when assessing planning applications
- increased community involvement in development issues
- the development of Catchment Management Plans
- the opportunity for integrated catchment management planning
- protection of the environment
- increased public awareness of the water environment
- help in identifying appropriate environmental indicators.

Current sustainability principles for water resources:

1 There should be no long term deterioration of the water environment resulting from water use or in water resources for future use

2 Reasonable demands for water from both existing and new social and economic development should be satisfied

3 Priority should be given to the management of water demand, to ensure the best use is being made of existing resources. Only if additional water resources are still required will new water resource development be considered

4 In managing water resources, opportunities to enhance the water environment should be identified.

Where new development would be at direct or unacceptable risk from flooding or would aggravate the risk of flooding elsewhere to an unacceptable level, proposals should be resisted.

Current sustainability principles for flood defence:

1 Effective defence for people and property against flooding from rivers and the sea should be provided, together with adequate arrangements for flood forecasting and warning

2 Inappropriate development within floodplains should be resisted where such developments would be at risk from flooding or may cause flooding elsewhere

3 Flood defence is an intervention in natural processes and therefore a balance has to be struck between maintaining and supporting natural floodplains and alleviating flood risk

4 Floodplains should be safeguarded to protect their vital role in allowing for the storage and free-flow of flood waters

5 To minimise increased surface water run-off, new development must be carefully located and designed. Where appropriate, source control measures should be incorporated into the scheme.

Figure 2.25 *Guidance for development plans*
Source: National Rivers Authority, 1995, Thames 21 – A planning perspective and a sustainable strategy for the Thames Region, National Rivers Authority

Managing an urban catchment: the Wandle Valley

Urban rivers and streams are at the mercy of strong development pressures and complex planning issues.

The River Wandle in London is typical of many urban rivers:

- it provides a valuable green corridor through an urban area
- it links a number of sites of conservation interest, such as Beddington Sewage Treatment Works, Wilderness Island Nature Reserve and Watermeads
- much of it has been described as a Site of Metropolitan Interest due to the variety of its plant life
- water quality is classified by the EA as poor to fair
- there is widespread contamination of groundwater, largely as a result of past industrial activity, e.g. at Beddington, from the sewage works and former mills.

The Wandle has been relatively unaffected by large-scale developments, but in 1985 permission was granted for the future extraction of underlying sands and gravels on condition that the pits are turned into lakes when extraction is complete. Critics argue that the lakes will not be large enough to provide adequate flood storage (i.e. the temporary storage of water after a flood or storm), nor will they be large enough to dilute the contaminants of the River Wandle. In addition, one water company has received permission to fill a number of the pits with domestic waste, and to develop them into landfill sites.

Any attempt to manage the River Wandle needs to balance the conflicting needs of the many interests (Figure 2.26). Flood storage, pollution control, conservation and recreation must be developed alongside the need to dispose of waste materials and fulfil the demand for aggregates for Britain's expanding housing market.

Figure 2.26 *The River Wandle, emerging from beneath the Arndale Centre, Wandsworth*

Inset 2.6
Planning issues in the River Wandle catchment

There are a number of sites for redevelopment along the River Wandle, providing opportunities for environmental enhancement and access to the river frontage.

The proposed gravel extraction and landfill operations will have a great impact, but opportunities should be identified for enhancing the River Wandle corridor. In particular, the proposals present an opportunity to create a large body of water for recreation in an area of London identified by the Sports Council as deficient in this respect. Informal access could also be improved.

The proposal for waste disposal is of concern both in terms of pollution and flooding. The guidelines set out in the NRA's *Policy and practice for the protection of groundwater* must be followed to try to protect the groundwater and surface water in the area from pollution. Any further encroachments into the floodplain should be resisted in order to retain the capacity as far as possible and allow the free flow of the flood waters.

Increases in surface water run-off caused by development should be contained by using source control measures (such as planting of vegetation) so that the risk of flooding is not increased further.

The diversity of flora and fauna should be protected and enhanced where development provides the opportunity.

Source: National Rivers Authority, 1995, Thames 21 – A planning perspective and a sustainable strategy for the Thames region, National Rivers Authority

Managing a rural catchment: the Upper Thames

The Upper Thames catchment is important for fisheries, wildlife conservation, as a major source of drinking water, recreation and navigation. The EA's CMP for the Upper Thames is not only to maintain the existing value of the catchment but also to protect and improve water quality and fish stocks, improve flood defences, enhance the recreation and conservation value of the Upper Thames and to ensure environmentally sustainable policies for water resources and future developments, particularly within the Cotswold Water Park (Figure 2.27, see page 48).

The Cotswold Water Park has been created by the extraction of gravel in the Upper Thames area. It covers nearly 6000 hectares and is the largest concentration of gravel pits and associated land in the UK. The characteristics of the Park are:

- the western part is covered by two Groundwater Protection Zones based around Somerford Keynes and Cerney Wick. In these zones, the use of nitrate fertilisers is banned
- the quality of surface and groundwater is generally high
- the River Thames and numerous tributaries flow the length of the Park and a large proportion of the Park falls within the floodplain. The floodplain provides an important flood alleviation facility which allows discharges on to the floodplain prior to reaching major urban areas downstream
- the area is an extremely important recreational resource within the region. Many of the lakes are already used for a wide range of water-based recreational activities. Informal recreation is also important and the two country parks attract many visitors. The Thames Path runs through the area
- the disused Thames and Severn Canal bisects the Park; there are various proposals for its restoration
- the Park supports a wide diversity of wildlife and habitat features of acknowledged national and international importance. Water areas are ecologically important for wildfowl, and a number of wet meadows have been designated as Sites of Special Scientific Interest (Figure 2.28).

The Cotswold Water Park is under considerable pressure because of the variety of developments which are focused on this environmentally sensitive area. For example, Gloucestershire and Wiltshire county councils have indicated an intention to extend the proposed area of mineral working to include an additional 4000 hectares of land to the east of the A419 in response to the anticipated demand for aggregates. (However, it must be remembered that the Park would not exist without its history of mineral workings.) In addition, the Park has great potential for recreation and tourism development, including significant built developments, such as the Lakewood Holiday Village, and an hotel and restaurant development on the 'gateway' site. Proposed road schemes, such as improvements to the A419 and several village by-passes, together with the proposed Latton by-pass, will improve accessibility. The EA's plans to divert water from the River Severn to the Thames to meet demand would also have an impact on the area.

The main concern of the EA is to balance the demand for further development with the protection of the water environment. Additional mineral extraction, for example, could make a significant impact on the landscape of the river corridor unless guidelines are followed and suitable uses for the area are agreed before extraction takes place. Further recreation and tourism development is also likely to have an

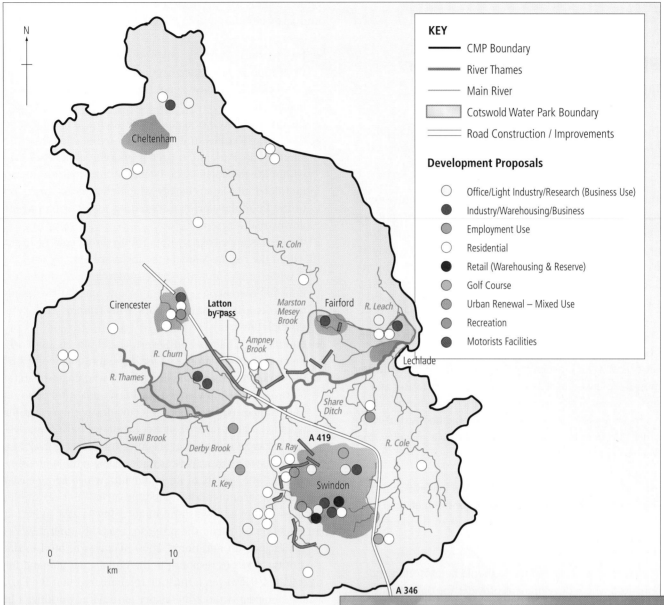

Figure 2.27 *The Cotswold Water Park*
Source: National Rivers Authority, 1996

impact on the water environment, including surface water run-off from built development and disturbance to wildlife by noisy sports. The EA must therefore work closely with local authorities to ensure that the correct balance is struck to minimise the impact on the water environment within the catchment.

Many of the responses to the NRA's Upper Thames Consultation Report of 1995 highlighted concerns relating to the Park; the Upper Thames Land Use Initiative put forward a vision for the Park which would ensure that any future development would be environmentally sustainable and take account of the sensitivity of the area. It was based on a site by site analysis of the areas searched for minerals.

Figure 2.28 *Cotswold Water Park – a former series of sand and gravel pits mana and used for recreation, the industry of the 90s.*

Inset 2.7
Planning issues in the Cotswold Water Park

The preservation and enhancement of the water environment is the top priority in an area of landscape, historic and cultural value. Any development proposals which would adversely affect the landscape of the Upper Thames Valley should be resisted. The restoration of mineral workings should lead to significant landscape enhancements.

Any further development should not result in irreversible damage to the high ecological value of the area. Buffer zones should be incorporated in all mineral extraction schemes to protect water courses and sites of nature conservation. Opportunities to create diverse wildlife habitats through restoration of gravel workings should be promoted.

The mineral extraction and restoration in the area, together with other developments such as highway improvements and recreation, pose a potential threat to the quality and quantity of surface and groundwater. All discharges will need consent to protect surface water. The guidelines set out in the NRA's *Policy and practice for the protection of groundwater* need to be followed, especially in areas covered by the Groundwater Protection Zones.

Investigations into groundwater levels and groundwater movements need to be carried out.

The development proposals should not result in an increased risk of flooding, reduce the storage capacity of the floodplain or interfere with flow routes. Where opportunities arise, the alleviation of existing flood risk should be provided. The water storage capacity of the area needs to be maintained in the interests of water resources as well as land drainage.

The route of the Thames Path should be protected from adverse change, and opportunities to enhance it and other rights-of-way should be maximised.

Environmental objectives
Water abstraction
- To manage water resources to achieve the right balance between the needs of the environment and those of the abstractor.
- To ensure that licence holders understand and comply with the terms and conditions of the licences.
- To ensure that abstraction does not cause any deterioration of water quality or have an adverse impact on aquatic or other water-dependent habitats.

Mineral extraction and solid waste disposal
- To ensure the sustainable use of resources whilst protecting the existing nature conservation value of the CWP (especially its nationally important bird populations), maintain the landscape quality along the Thames and maximise the potential for enhancing the conservation value of the area by influencing restoration of future working, where appropriate, to provide wetland and open water habitat mosaics.
- To control and influence mineral extraction, restoration and after-use and solid waste disposal in other areas of the catchment in such a way that other uses or resources are not compromised.

Future water resources in the Thames Region sets out a strategy for future planning and sustainable management. The strategy aims to:
- sustain the natural resource for future use
- provide a flexible framework for water resources management and development in the region
- secure proper safeguards for the water environment
- identify opportunities to enhance the water environment, particularly in association with new schemes but also to address existing problems such as low flow rivers
- respond to reasonable expectations of social and economic development.

QUESTIONS

1 In what ways do the development issues in rural catchments differ from those of urban catchments?

2 What is the ecological role of rivers?

3 In what ways are pressures on rivers likely to change in the twenty-first century? (Look again at Chapter 1, *Britain's changing climate*, for some ideas.)

SUMMARY

In this chapter we have looked at the human impact on hydrology and rivers. The effect has been both long-term and significant. So great has the impact been that we can talk of urban hydrology and urban rivers. We can also talk about rural hydrology and rural streams which are also far from natural. There is an increasing realisation that the human impact has so far been largely negative, but that it is also possible to rectify the situation. Our examples of river restoration show the benefits of natural rivers and how rivers can be restored. Similarly, the development of Catchment Management Plans allows planners and interested parties to develop rivers in a sustainable way.

QUESTIONS

1 Why is a straight river channel more useful to a mill owner than a meandering one?
2 Discuss the value of river restoration. Who are the winners and the losers when rivers are restored to their natural state?
3 What is the likely impact of global warming on river catchments in the UK?

INVESTIGATIVE WORK

For a stream near you, find out what impact human activity has had on the stream. When did this occur?

Compare the nature and characteristics of a rural stream with that of an urban stream.

Measure the discharge of a small stream, or the run-off from a drain or gutter, during the course of a storm. How does the discharge vary as the storm progresses?

Contact your local Environment Agency office (check the Yellow Pages or similar). Ask them for a copy of the Catchment Management Plan for your area. What are the development issues of your catchment? How have these issues developed? What can be done about them?

BIBLIOGRAPHY AND RECOMMENDED READING

Burt, T. and Haycock N., 1990, Farming and nitrate pollution, *Geography,* 76, 60-3.

Goudie, A., 1997, *The human impact reader: readings and case studies,* Blackwell

Gleick, P., (Ed.), 1993, *Water in crisis: a guide to the world's fresh water resources,* OUP

Hollis, G., 1988, Rain, roads and run off: hydrology in cities, *Geography,* 73, 9-18

Nagle, G. and Spencer, K., 1997, *Sustainable development,* Hodder and Stoughton

National Rivers Authority, 1994, *Future water resources in the Thames Region: a strategy for sustainable management,* National Rivers Authority

National Rivers Authority, 1995, *Thames 21 – A planning perspective and a sustainable strategy for the Thames region,* National Rivers Authority

National Rivers Authority, 1995, *Policy and practice for the protection of groundwater,* National Rivers Authority

National Rivers Authority, 1996, *Upper Thames Catchment Management Plan: summary,* National Rivers Authority

National Rivers Authority, 1996, *Upper Thames Catchment Management Plan: Action Plan,* National Rivers Authority

OFWAT, 1996, *Memorandum of evidence for the inquiry into water conservation and supply by the House of Commons Environment Committee*

WEB SITES

River Severn river link -
http://mail.bris.ac.uk/0/6/7Extss/river/.html
US flood insurance data -
http://www.insure.com/home/flood/stats.html

Chapter 3
Changing landforms

Some landforms change very slowly; others change rapidly, as, for example, during a landslide. The changes they undergo can be natural or they can be the result of human activity. Indeed, in some cases it may be difficult to tell the difference between natural processes and human activities: it may, of course, be a combination of the two. In this chapter we look at a number of landforms and processes in the UK that are the results of, or affected by, human intervention. These include slopes, landslides, quarrying and changes in coastal areas.

THE HUMAN IMPACT ON LANDFORMS

There are very few areas of human activity which do not have an impact on environments and landforms. Landforms can be created by constructional activities, such as tipping or excavation, by hydrological interference, and by farming. For example, hillsides have been terraced in many parts of the world for many centuries.

The landscape-forming processes are a product of geological structure and geomorphological processes on that structure over a period of time. It is only the geomorphological processes that can be modified to any extent by human activity – although they are largely climatically determined, by factors such as weathering, or gravity controlled, by for example mass movement, and are therefore not readily controllable.

Man-made changes in landforms can be deliberate or unintentional (Figure 3.1). Artificial valleys can be created by road or rail cuttings, such as the M3 at Twyford Down, and drainage systems may be constructed to control the hydrology of an area (Figure 3.2). New land may be created by the deliberate infilling of marshes or lagoons, or may be generated unintentionally by estuarine deposition of excess sediment load carried by rivers as a result of high levels of soil erosion. Hollows may be excavated for mineral extraction or may result from land subsidence due to mining or land drainage.

The shape of the earth's surface has had a major impact upon human activity. Many ancient settlements, such as Iron Age hill forts, are located on hilltops. Lines of communication are strongly influenced by the shape of the land, for example, the prehistoric Icknield Way which follows part of the chalk ridge of the Chilterns, and the canals and railways of the industrial revolution. In more recent times, the siting of airports and nuclear plants has been heavily influenced by physical geography. Airports require large areas of flat, solid

1. **Direct anthropogenic (human) processes:**
   1.1. Constructional
   Tipping, compacted, molten
   Graded: moulded, ploughed, terraced
   1.2. Excavational
   Digging, cutting, mining, blasting of cohesive or non-cohesive materials
   Cratered
   Tramped, churned
   1.3. Hydrological interference
   Flooding, damming, canal construction
   Dredging, channel modification
   Draining
   Coastal protection

2. **Indirect anthropogenic processes:**
   2.1. Acceleration of erosion and sedimentation
   Agricultural activity and clearance of vegetation
   Engineering, especially road construction and urbanisation
   Incidental modification of hydrological regime
   2.2. Subsidence: collapse, settling
   Mining
   Hydraulic
   Thermokarst (depressions formed by the thawing of ice in the ground)
   2.3. Slope failure: landslide, flow, accelerated creep
   Loading
   Undercutting
   Shaking
   Lubrication
   2.4. Earthquake generation: loading (reservoirs)
   Lubrication (fault plain)

Figure 3.1 *A classification of landforms and processes resulting from human activities*
Source: Goudie, A., 1993, The human impact on the natural environment, Blackwell

Figure 3.2 *The M3 motorway cutting through the chalk downland.*

Feature	Cause
Pits and ponds	Mining, marling
Broads	Peat extraction
Spoil heaps	Mining
Terracing lynchets	Agriculture
Ridge and furrow	Agriculture
Cuttings	Transport
Embankments	Transport, river or coast management
Dikes	River and coast management
Mounds	Defence, memorials
Craters	War
City mounds	Human occupation
Canals	Transport, irrigation
Reservoirs	Water management
Subsidence, depressions	Mineral and water extraction
Moats	Defence
Banks on roads	Noise abatement

marling – adding lime to acid, often boggy soils
lynchets – cultivation terraces dating from Celtic times 3000 BC
ridge and furrow – a cultivation technique which creates raised ridges to
    increase soil temperature and improve moisture conditions; the ridges are
    separated by furrows

Figure 3.3 *Some 'human' landforms*
Source: Goudie, A., 1993, The human impact on the natural environment, Blackwell

ground, while nuclear power stations need tectonically safe locations, with plenty of water (preferably in a remote area).

The shape of the land may also provide opportunities or impose restraints upon towns and cities, while slope geometry is important in relation to soil control in rural areas – slope angles are modified by terracing and surfaces are affected by mining and quarrying. Some landforms are solely the result of human activity (Figure 3.3).

Our ability to affect the natural environment has increased as technology has developed, but in spite of all our activities, direct changes to the shape of the land surface have been small when compared to the scale of natural landforms. However, the indirect modification of process and form by human activity is a significant factor in causing landforms to change. Indirect human activities are often difficult to recognise but they may lead to an acceleration of natural processes. For example, removing natural vegetation cover through cutting, burning and grazing can lead to increased erosion and sedimentation. Human activity can often set into motion a train of natural events, for example, attempts to protect coastal areas in one part may lead to increased erosion elsewhere.

WEATHERING

Weathering is the breakdown of rock in its original situation, and weathering processes can be intensified by human activities. Changes in the nature and rate of weathering are closely linked to air quality. Increased emissions of SO_2

Figure 3.4 *The effects of weathering*

(from the burning of fossil fuels) has led to higher levels of sulphuric acid. Chemical reactions with SO_2 can create salts, such as calcium sulphate and magnesium sulphate. These are able to chemically weather rocks (Figure 3.4). Similarly, as atmospheric levels of CO_2 have risen, the potential for carbonation increases. Carbonation is the process whereby atmospheric CO_2 combines with water to form a weak carbonic acid. This attacks rocks chemically, especially those with calcium carbonate, such as limestones and chalk. Thus, as levels of atmospheric CO_2 rise, so does the potential for increased weathering.

Mass movement

Mass movement is the movement under gravity of material on a slope. The rate and nature of such movement varies with the nature of the material, the topography of the climate and the vegetation; it can be very slow (creep) or very rapid (slides and slumps). Rates of mass movements can be altered by building or excavation, drainage or agriculture. Mass move-

Type of movement	Method of control
Falls	Flattening the slope Benching the slope Drainage Reinforcement of rock walls by grouting with cement, anchor bolts Covering of wall with steel mesh
Slides and flows	Grading or benching to flatten the slope Drainage of surface water with ditches Sealing surface cracks to prevent infiltration Sub-surface drainage Rock or earth buttresses at foot Retaining walls at foot Pilings through the potential slide mass

Figure 3.5 *Methods of controlling mass movement*
Source: Goudie, A., 1993, The human impact on the natural environment, Blackwell

ments can be accelerated when slopes have been desta-bilised by weathering or human activity. Human activity, such as creating roads and railway cuttings, leads to rapid changes. Local erosion can be intensified by footpath tram-pling in recreational areas of the countryside. Some mass movements are created by humans piling up waste soil and rock into unstable accumulations that move without warn-ing. Landslides can be created by undercutting or overloading. As well as causing mass movement, human activities can reduce them (Figure 3.5). (See Chapter 4 in *Hazards* in this series for a full discussion.)

DIRECT MODIFICATION

Slopes

Most of the changes to slopes caused by human activities have been very minor in relation to the scale of the natural events. Human interference with slopes tends to have been most effective in speeding up naturally occurring processes rather than creating new features.

Transport developments however can lead to the cre-ation of entirely new landforms (Figure 3.6). Building and road construction in urban areas leads to a great deal of slope modification; to ensure safety, extensive engineering work has to be implemented. Almost all buildings with foundations cause some modification to the natural slope of the land, and even on flat sites, large modern buildings generally involve the removal of material to allow for proper foundations. On steeper slopes, a cut-and-fill technique is often used to provide a horizontal base (Figure 3.7), creat-ing a small level terrace with an over-steepened slope at both ends. The steep slopes, devoid of soil and vegetation, are potentially much less stable than the former natural slope and are, in times of intense rainfall, susceptible to small, but quite damaging, landslips.

Figure 3.6 *Railway cutting, Combe, Oxfordshire – a manmade landform*

Figure 3.7 *Slope instability caused by road building*
Source: Goudie, A., 1993, The human impact on the natural environment, Blackwell

Excavation and dumping

People have been excavating and dumping for thousands of years – for construction, mining and quarrying – creating some of the most significant and extensive man-made land-forms in the UK. Construction and dumping produced Newgrange in County Meath, Ireland, and the Iron Age fort at Maiden Castle in Dorset. The former looks like a low, rounded hill, whilst the latter is a series of steep 15 metre ramparts surrounding a chalk hill. Many pits have been excavated in the past in the search for materials; some of the pits excavated in one era are filled in by later generations. For example, many of the depressions caused by marl (lime) diggers in south-west Lancashire and north-west Cheshire have been filled in. Less than 40% of the 5000 depressions formed in the mid-nineteenth century still exist.

In more recent years the environmental impact of exca-vation and dumping has been dramatic. The destruction caused by strip mining, for example, far exceeds any other direct form of impact that humans have on landforms. Strip, or opencast, mining involves the removal of materials from the surface. The overburden (soil and rock lying over the mineral mined) is removed, and the exposed reserves are excavated. As early as 1922, R. L. Sherlock estimated that in the UK as much as 31 billion tonnes of rock had been excavated as a result of human activity (Figure 3.9, see page 54). This is likely to be a severe underestimate. Even then he stated that 'man is many times more powerful, as an agent of denudation, than all the atmospheric forces combined' (quoted in Goudie, A., 1993, *The human impact*, Blackwell).

One of the largest quarries in Britain is the Delabole Slate Quarry in Cornwall which is over 150 metres deep and has a circumference of 26 kilometres. The most important effect of mining and quarrying on landforms is the dumping of waste material. In the UK, there are over 2000 million tonnes of spoil heaps, rising as much as 30-40 metres above the surrounding area. Rates of sedimentation in rivers asso-ciated with mining activities are very high; when mining activities cease, rates decrease rapidly.

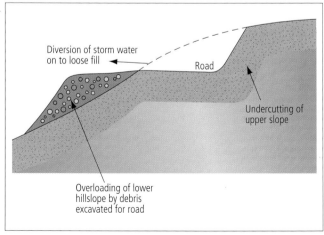

The largest single engineering project in Britain has been the digging of the Channel Tunnel. The material excavated for this project has allowed new landforms to be created. Samphire Hoe, formerly the Samphire Cliff construction site, is an artificially-created 35 hectare piece of land between Folkestone and Dover (Figure 3.8). It was created from over 5 million cubic metres of the 8.75 million cubic metres dug from the tunnel. The Hoe reaches 28 metres at its highest point and has been landscaped to provide a variety of habitats, including three ponds. The Hoe is protected from wave erosion by a sea wall of almost 225 000 cubic metres of concrete. Access to the Hoe is through a 130 metre tunnel, itself created as part of the 1974 Channel Tunnel project.

Activity	Approximate volume m³	% of total
Mines	5 147 000 000	
Quarries and pits	11 920 000 000	
Railways	2 331 000 000	
Manchester Ship Canal	41 154 000	
Other canals	153 800 000	
Road cuttings	480 000 000	
Docks and harbours	77 000 000	
Foundations of buildings and street excavations	385 000 000	
Total	30 534 954 000	

Figure 3.9 *Total excavation of material in the UK pre-1922*
Source: Goudie, A., 1993, The human impact on the natural environment, Blackwell

Inset 3.1
The M74 Motorway

The new M74 is a 90 kilometre motorway linking Scotland's motorways with the M6 in England. The Millbank to Nether Abington section is just 11.5 kilometres long and required the following materials to build it:

- 320 000 tonnes of sand and gravel
- 375 000 tonnes of rock used for foundation and earth works
- 135 000 tonnes of recycled slag used as sub-base for the road
- 4500 tonnes of hard rock chippings used on the central reservation
- 390 000 tonnes of bitumen-coated stone used in surfacing the road.

QUESTIONS

1 How much sand and gravel and other rock are needed to build 1 kilometre of the motorway?
2 How much is needed to build 90 kilometres?

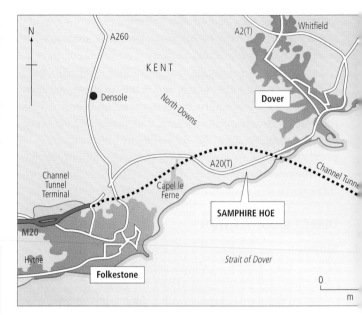

Figure 3.8 *Samphire Hoe – a new landform*
Source: Times Educational Supplement, October 1997

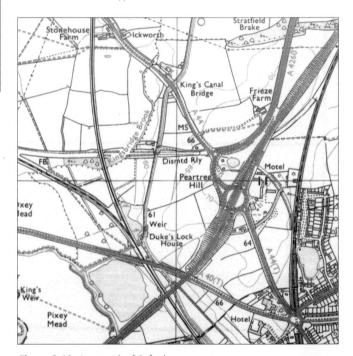

Figure 3.10 *Area north of Oxford*
Source: Ordnance Survey, 1992

QUESTIONS

1 Complete Figure 3.9 by working out the percentage that each activity contributed to the total. Show your results on a pie chart.

2 Study Figure 3.10, an extract from an Ordnance Survey map. State **three** ways in which the construction of the railway has modified existing landforms.

Quarrying

Quarrying is an important part of the UK economy – the sale of aggregates alone is worth over £2000 million per year. Demand for these materials has increased from 20 million tonnes in 1900 to 300 million tonnes in 1989. The production of aggregates for concrete includes the extraction of sand and gravel, crushed limestone, artificial and manufactured aggregates, and crushed sandstone. There are over 1200 quarries in Britain and about 26 000 people employed in the quarrying industry.

The geology of the UK can be roughly divided into two parts by drawing a line from Lincolnshire to Dorset. To the south-east of the line, the rocks are mainly sedimentary, which includes chalk, clay, sand and gravel; to the north and west of the line can be found the older and harder igneous rocks, such as granite, and metamorphic rock such as slate. The south-east of the UK is the largest market for construction materials, and demand cannot be met from local sources. In particular, road building and maintenance require crushed hard rock such as granite and limestone. The economic cost of moving heavy low-value aggregates by road is very high and the price of a lorry load of crushed rock may double after only a 20-30 kilometre journey. For these reasons, it is important for a quarry to be as near as possible to its market. Where a quarry will be sited depends on a number of factors:

- size, thickness and quality of deposit
- how much overburden (soil and topsoil covering the deposit) will need to be removed
- how close it will be to potential customers
- local transport links
- environmental considerations
- applications being passed by the planning authorities.

Meeting rising demand

The demand for aggregates is forecast to rise from nearly 300 million tonnes in 1989 to 400 million tonnes per year by the year 2010. There are a number of possible solutions for providing more aggregates from alternative sources. One solution to cope with the increase will be in the creation of large coastal quarries, sometimes referred to as super quarries. Glensanda is a major coastal quarry and is situated on the west coast of Scotland (Figure 3.11). It is planned to have a life of about 150 years and the hole left behind will be about three kilometres by one kilometre wide and 300 metres deep. The quarry has no road leading to it. Plant and machinery going in and rock coming out are all transported by sea. Crushed granite is sent out in specially designed 75 000 tonne ships. About half is sent to south-east England and the rest is sent to Germany, the Netherlands, France, Denmark, Poland and even the Caribbean.

Coastal quarries have a number of advantages:

- they are sited away from densely populated areas
- the distribution of aggregate by sea is cheap and more energy efficient than by road
- quarries provide employment in local communities
- because the workings are deep they do not use the same area of land as shallow workings
- they will allow the UK to become self-sufficient in aggregates.

However, there are a number of disadvantages:

- not all ports can handle such large ships
- although the quarries are situated in sparsely populated areas, many are of great scenic value and support valuable wildlife.

Alternative sources of materials include:

- the use of marine dredged sand and gravel
- slag from blast furnaces in the steel industry
- recycling materials from demolished buildings
- making use of mine waste.

Even with materials supplied from these alternative sources, the majority of aggregates will still have to come from traditional land-based quarries.

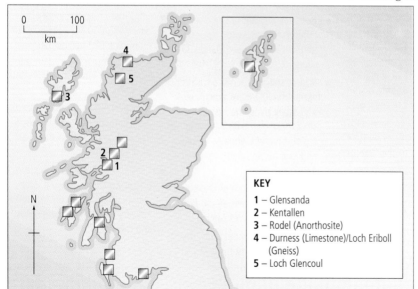

Figure 3.11 *The location of super quarries*
Source: Ecology and environmental science factsheet 47, September 1995

Inset 3.2
Ingham Quarry and Cliffe Hill Quarry

Ingham Quarry is a modern sand and gravel pit in Suffolk. The site was first identified as a potential quarry in 1983. Suffolk County Council imposed twenty-nine conditions as part of the permission to work it. These regulate the hours it can be worked, how the site is to be restored after excavation has finished, noise control and even the colour of the plant and machinery that have to be used. The sand and gravel has to be quarried by removing the overburden. This material includes top soil and subsoil and is stored on site so that it can be used in future to make screening banks and for restoration. When the material is extracted from the quarry it is brought to drag lines which take the load to a screening plant where machines wash and sort the material into different sizes.

By contrast, Cliffe Hill Quarry in Leicestershire supplies igneous rock called diorite. By the 1980s production was approaching one million tonnes per year but the company wanted to extend the quarry by opening a new quarry nearby. Quarrying at the new site began in 1989. One of the problems is that there is a village between the two sites. An environmental impact assessment (1991) investigated problems such as:

- how the site could be screened
- how farming interests could be protected
- how quarrying affected water quality and local streams
- how dust and blasting could be controlled
- how traffic could be managed.

As a result of the eighteen-month assessment survey, over sixty detailed planning requirements were laid down.

Blasting occurs once a day and this brings down between 10 000 and 20 000 tonnes of rock. In fact, it takes just one kilogram of explosive to produce ten tonnes of broken rock. The rock goes through a series of crushing and screening machines until it is broken down into nine sizes of stone ranging from fine dust to 50 millimetres across. Although the main markets are in the East Midlands, train loads of stone are taken to the south-east of England.

QUESTION

1 **Using the data in Figure 3.12, discuss the physical and economic impact of quarrying on the environment.**

Ingham Quarry

- Costs to set up £1.7 million
- Production per year 150 000 –250 000 tonnes
- Products: Sand, gravel, concrete. The site also acts as a sales point for the company's other products such as limestone
- Reserves and life of site 2 million tonnes which will last 10–15 years depending on the demand
- Size of site 86 acres: 46 acres extraction, 6 acres machinery and stock piles, 10 acres strong soil and overburden to use in restoration, 22 acres of environmental screen banks
- Restoration Nature reserve, woodland and farmland
- Reducing the impact on the environment Soundproofing on machinery, embankments and trees to hide the site.
- Employment More than thirty jobs depend on the site although only six people are employed directly in the quarrying
- Contribution to the local economy Approximately £50 000 per year paid in rates. The quarry has a turnover of about £1 million per year with some of that going into the local economy in the form of wages paid to employees
- Transport About five lorry loads leave the site each day but this varies according to the time of year
- Use of products Most of the quarry products are distributed into the local area for the production of concrete.

Cliffe Hill Quarry

- Costs to set up £45 million
- Production per year Up to 4 million tonnes
- Products: Nine sizes of crushed stone for roads, ready-mixed concrete and rail ballast
- Reserves and life of site Over 1 million tonnes, with an estimated life of between 20 and 30 years
- Size of site 500 acres; 54 acres extraction, 23 acres machinery and stock piles, the rest of the site is taken up with land waiting to be used, storage of soil and overburden and screening and landscaping
- Restoration Because of the long life of this site there are no firm details as to final restoration
- Reducing the impact on the environment Measures taken to control noise, dust and vibration, banks contoured and planted to hide site from view, rail link to reduce lorry traffic
- Employment More than 150 jobs depend on the site
- Contribution to the local economy £425 000 per year paid in rates, plus £2.5 million per year paid in wages to employees. Turnover of about £18 million per year
- Transport Up to three hundred lorry loads leave the site each day and on most days one train load leaves the site
- Uses of products Products are distributed over a wide area, mainly used in the construction industry and for repairing roads and railways.

Figure 3.12 *Facts about Ingham and Cliffe Hill quarries*
Source: Middleton, G., 1992, About quarrying, Hobson

Case study:
Ready Mixed Concrete, the Breamish Valley and Druridge Bay

The Breamish Valley in the Northumberland hills is a site of scenic beauty and cultural heritage. Among the fells there are a number of excellent archaeological sites, including hilltop forts and ancient field boundaries, created by centuries of ploughing. The area also includes many rare species of plants, birds and mammals. In 1996, Northern Aggregates, a subsidiary of the Ready Mixed Concrete (RMC) company, applied for planning permission to extract gravel from the area (Figure 3.13). The plan is to extract 1.5 million tonnes of sand and gravel from a 60 hectare site over a period of ten years.

In addition to objections by archaeologists, many local people objected to the proposals, and Berwick Borough Council lodged a formal objection with the Northumberland County Council. The Ministry of Agriculture, Fisheries and Food objected to the plan on agricultural grounds, and the Northumberland National Park Authority objected on the grounds of traffic, noise, damage to tourism and the character of the landscape. However, an environmental statement carried out in consultation with the Environment Agency and others came out in favour of the proposal. According to RMC, more jobs are needed for local people, especially in the recession-hit North-East.

Figure 3.13 *The Breamish Valley, Northumberland*

RMC has operated in the North-East for a long time. Some of their activities have created much controversy. In the 1970s, RMC bought the rights to extract sand from Druridge Bay. Those rights had originally been granted to a small company. Up to 40 000 tonnes of sand were removed from the Bay each year. As a result of the quarrying, there has been severe erosion of certain parts of the beach, and valuable habitats are at risk. The area is home to a colony of orchids and a proposed sanctuary for otters and bitterns. In 1993, RMC withdrew from Druridge Bay following sustained local opposition. According to some protesters, RMC were prepared to leave Druridge Bay only because they were being allowed into another part of Northumberland.

Druridge Bay has been the subject of other plans. For example, Magnox Electric planned to develop a nuclear power station there. However, in 1996 they agreed to sell their 140 hectare site. In addition, RMC announced that it was giving up its rights on a 1.5 kilometre stretch of the 12 kilometre Druridge Bay. By that time, over 1.5 million tonnes of sand had been removed from the Bay, reducing the attraction of one of the North-East's most popular beaches.

Elsewhere, RMC have had a different effect upon the environment. It has received praise and awards for its landscaping and redevelopment of Thorpe Park in Surrey. Bought in the 1930s for gravel extraction, the flooded gravel pits were developed in the 1970s for leisure use. Millions of tonnes of soil were moved, new lake margins were formed, land was drained and over 10 000 trees were planted. In 1979 when the park was opened, it won an award for best new tourist attraction in the UK. At Great Amwell in Hertfordshire, a 50 hectare conservation area has been developed on the site of a former sand and gravel quarry. Elsewhere, former gravel pits have been turned into a number of leisure features such as trout farms, water sports centres, and golf courses.

QUESTIONS

1 Contact your local County Council to find out the environmental standards and requirements for mineral workings in your area.

2 What do you think makes 'an environmentally sound transport strategy'?

3 Why is there so much opposition to mineral extractors if, like RMC, they are prepared to redevelop and landscape the sites after use?

We will undertake to:

- Minimise the impact of unavoidable disturbances which may result from any of our operations.
- Protect natural resources and ensure that, where possible, there is no lasting environmental damage to flora, fauna, soil, water, or air.
- Introduce processes which minimise waste and incorporate the recycling of materials wherever possible, and where wastes are not eliminated, provide environmentally sound treatment and disposal, or find markets for their use as a resource.
- Operate businesses efficiently and seek to reduce energy consumption.
- Use the best practicable clean technology to minimise or abate the production or emission of pollutants.
- Restore land after mineral extraction to a high quality to be used either for agriculture, nature reserves, leisure or sporting facilities, or general building purposes.
- Operate, where possible, above the environmental standards necessitated by legislation, statutory requirements and any relevant codes of practice.
- Continue our existing policy of encouraging participation in the local community and conservation projects.
- Develop our links with the educational system to assist in the understanding of the interaction between industry and society.
- Develop environmental plans and set targets for the Division's activities.
- Assess and have an environmental awareness of the products and services undertaken and used by the Division.
- Maintain an environmentally sound transport strategy.
- Include environmental considerations in investment decisions.
- Afford a high priority to site care and good housekeeping.

Figure 3.14 *RMC's Environmental policy*
Source: Ready Mixed Concrete, 1997, Safeguarding our future

Coal mining

As we have seen, mining has a number of environmental impacts (Figure 3.9, see page 54), most notably the tipping of waste materials. Mining for coal, the predominant material mined in the UK, has other environmental effects. Where the overburden is shallow (less than 15 metres), small depressions form over the mined area. These may develop for up to fifty years after the mining has stopped. There is also a considerable impact on water resources, both quantity and quality. Up to 17 litres of water are needed for each tonne of coal mined. Underground mining uses 63–120 litres/tonne and a further 33 litres/tonne for surface waste disposal.

Impact	Characteristics
Accumulation of CO_2 in the atmosphere	Effects potentially global, but unpredictable spatially and temporally. Resistant to technical amelioration.
Acid precipitation from SO_2 and NO_x; acid mine drainage	Regional damage (often across international boundaries) to forest productivity and fresh water fisheries. Emission control of gases feasible.
Land-use for mining operations	Local to regional scale. May be only temporary if reclamation is practised; technology for this is available.
Consumptive water use for conversion plants, open cast mining and reclamation	Regional impacts on agro- and other ecosystems where water is scarce. 'Mining' of aquifers is possible. Resistant to technical amelioration.

Figure 3.15 *Major environmental impacts of coal use (excluding human health)*
Source: Simmons, I., 1989, Changing the face of the earth: culture, environment, history, Blackwell

Type of effluent	Tonnes per GW(e) per year
Airborne effluents:	
Particulates	3×10^3
Sulphur oxides	11×10^4
Nitrogen oxides	2.7×10^4
Carbon monoxide	2×10^3
Hydrocarbons	400
Liquid effluents:	
Organic material	66.2
Sulphuric acid	82.5
Chlorides	26.3
Phosphates	41.7
Boron	331
Suspended solids	497
Solid waste (ash)	3.6×105

GW(e) Gigawatt of energy

Figure 3.16 *Effluents from a coal-fired power station*
Source: Simmons, I., 1989, Changing the face of the earth: culture, environment, history, Blackwell

Figure 3.17 *Environmental linkages in the extraction of coal*
Source: after US Office of Technology Assessment; Simmons, I., 1989, Changing the face of the earth: culture, environment, history, Blackwell

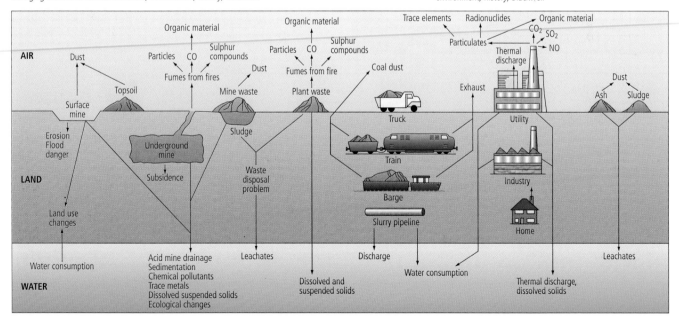

QUESTIONS

1 Using a dictionary, explain the meaning of the term 'technical amelioration'.

2 Study Figure 3.16 which shows effluents from a coal-fired power station.

a) Which is the largest emission from the station?

b) Why is a table a better way of showing this data than a pie chart?

3 Briefly outline some of the environmental implications of the data shown in Figure 3.17. (Think about pollution, subsidence, flooding: try to link cause with result).

Case study:
The Aberfan disaster, 1966

Figure 3.18 The Aberfan disaster, October 1966

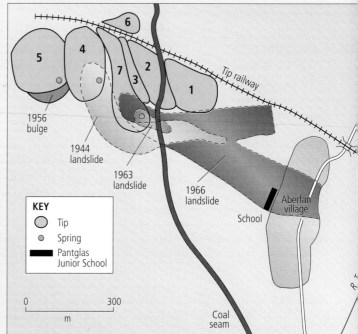

Figure 3.19 A plan view of Aberfan, the spoil heaps and the landslide
Source: after Waltham, 1978; Perry, A., 1981, Environmental hazards in the British Isles, George Allen and Unwin

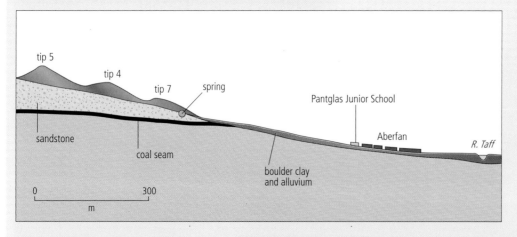

Figure 3.20 Geological cross section of the Aberfan area
Source: Perry, A., 1981, Environmental hazards in the British Isles, George Allen and Unwin

On 21st October 1966, a landslide involving a coal tip spoil heap at Aberfan, South Wales, killed 144 people, 116 of whom were pupils at the Pantglas Junior School (Figure 3.18). Aberfan lies on the banks of the River Taff and was overlooked by the tips of the Merthyr Vale Colliery (Figure 3.19).

The landslide involved over 100 000 cubic metres of colliery waste travelling at speeds of up to 30 kilometres/hour. Earlier landslides had occurred in the vicinity, but the National Coal Board believed that the speed of the landslide movements was slow enough to allow warnings to be given. However, spoil

heap number 7 was located above a spring, and water seeping through the sandstone emerged as a spring in the lower part of the tip (Figure 3.20). As the water passed through, it removed fine clay from the 'toe' of the tip, thereby increasing its steepness.

It was 9.15 and the school had just finished morning prayers when the million tons of coal waste, rocks and water crumpled 800 feet down the Aberfan mountain. The children were due to start their week's half-term holiday at noon. But many children never reached the school at all. Fog delayed a busload of 50 seniors and juniors from the village of Mount Pleasant nearby. Some decided to walk – and arrived late enough to miss the landfall.

Source: The Guardian, 22 October 1966

The National Coal Board (NCB) said last night that a build up of rain water inside the tip at Aberfan had probably burst the base of the tip and caused 2 million tons of waste to slide down the valley.

Source: The Guardian, 22 October 1966

Already by Friday morning there had been much more rain during October in the area of South Wales which includes Aberfan than it gets on average during the whole month – and more than half of this had fallen in one torrential downpour two days before.

Source: The Guardian, 24 October 1966

Figure 3.21 *Aberfan, 1966*

A coal tip engulfed the grounds of a school in South Wales only hours before 950 children were due to begin lessons yesterday.

The tip was dislodged by the torrential rain which continued to lash the south. And Gwent is just six miles from Aberfan where 128 children and 16 adults died when slurry buried their village school 26 years ago.

Parents taking their children to Tredegar Comprehensive School, Gwent, were faced by around 3000 tons of colliery spoil up to six feet deep which had poured down from the 100 ft tip ... the waste poured on to the grounds in a V-shape, sweeping through the school's mining museum.

A tide of coal waste 30 ft wide descended on the school and crushed the museum.

Engineers believe the slippage was caused by a blocked culvert which led to a build up of water. Twenty years ago, worried parents complained to the Government after a collapse at the tip just before the school was due to open. They were told by Mrs. Margaret Thatcher, the then Education Secretary, that the tip was safe.

Source: The Times, 3 December 1992

Figure 3.22 *Gwent, 1992*

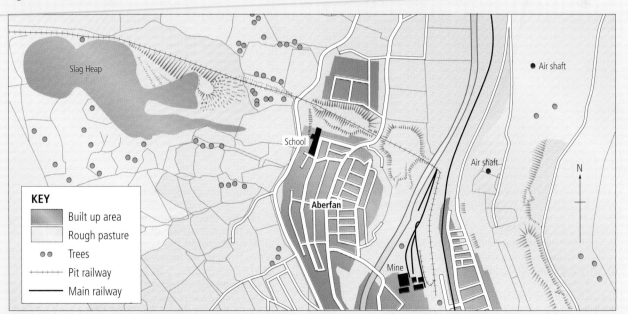

Figure 3.23 *Ordnance Survey map of Aberfan, 1964*
Source: Ordnance Survey, 1964

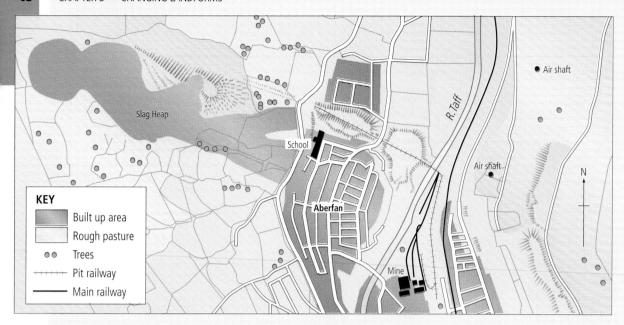

Figure 3.24
*Ordnance Survey
map of Aberfan,
1970*
*Source: Ordnance
Survey, 1970*

Figure 3.25
*Ordnance Survey
map of Aberfan,
1993*
*Source: Ordnance
Survey, 1993*

QUESTIONS

1 Study Figure 3.20. In what ways was the local geology important in adding to the disaster at Aberfan?

2 Study Figure 3.19.
   a) Explain the location of the spring. What impact did this have on the disaster that followed?
   b) Why are there no landslides associated with tips 1, 2, 3 and 6?

3 Explain why the removal of material at the toe of the spoil heap would increase the likelihood of a landslide.

4 Give two contrasting reasons to explain why the rate of landslides increased during the 1960s and 1970s.

5 a) Why did the NCB continue tipping coal dust onto a large source of water?

b) Why, after giving a written assurance in 1964 that tipping at Aberfan would cease, did they change their minds and continue routine tipping up to the morning of Friday, 21 October 1966?

6 In what ways did the causes of the 1992 landslide differ from those of the 1966 landslide?

7 Study Figures 3.23, 3.24 and 3.25.
   a) Describe the changes that have occurred in the Aberfan district since 1964.
   b) How did the slope (gradient) of the tip and the underlying ground contribute to the disaster? Support your answer with evidence from Figure 3.20.
   c) Comment on the path of the landslide as shown in Figures 3.18 and 3.24.

SUBSIDENCE

Ground subsidence in the UK can be natural, such as from the solution of limestone, or it can relate to human activities, such as the extraction of solids from below the ground (mining) or the abstraction or addition of liquids to the ground (flooding or drainage).

The impact of mining on subsidence depends on a variety of factors:

- the thickness of the seam
- the depth of the seam
- the width of the deposit
- the degree of infilling with solid material after working
- the geological structure
- the method of removal.

In general, the amount of subsidence is less than the thickness of the seam, and decreases with increasing depth of the seam. If subsidence occurs, the material does not form a compact layer (unlike the material removed). If the material mined is at great depth, the large depth of overburden may be sufficiently strong to remain in place. Thin layers of overmatter, by contrast, are much less stable.

Salt mining in Cheshire has caused much subsidence. Seams over 30 metres thick, a highly soluble rock (rock salt), and mining at a shallow depth (about 70 metres below the surface) have aided subsidence. Small-scale subsidence (up to 60 centimetres) took place during the 1930s along the flood plain of the River Stour in Kent following the mining of a 1.2–1.5 metre thick coal seam. Almost four square kilometres are now affected and are subject to flooding. Certain low-density, unconsolidated sediments may be stress-resistant when dry but when thoroughly wetted for the first time are weakened. During irrigation their (intergranular) strength falls, leading to rapid compaction and subsidence.

Very slight movement of the land beneath the foundations of a structure can be extremely damaging; the movement of buildings caused by the drying of clay soils and rocks during the dry summers of 1989 and 1990 is a good example. In the UK, extraction of water from the chalk aquifer under London is thought to have been responsible for causing subsidence over 450 square kilometres with a maximum drop of 0.35 metres.

Drainage and reclamation works carried out on wetlands, such as marsh and mud flats, in order to transform them into more profitable areas, often result in the compaction of recent deposits. Generally, the settlement rate is proportional to the drainage rate: the lower the water table, the greater the subsidence. Subsidence is always greater in areas of peat and organic soils because they undergo an irreversible oxidation from biochemical action on drying that reduces the volume. For example, in the peat Fenlands of Cambridgeshire and Lincolnshire a ground surface settlement ranging between five and ten metres has been observed since 1800. At Holme Fen Post in the Fenlands of Huntingdonshire, the level of the land has fallen by

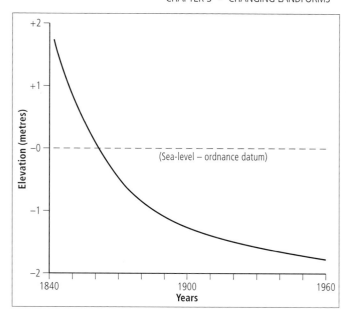

Figure 3.26 *Subsidence in the Fens at Holme Fen Post, 1842–1960*
Source: based on data in Fillenham, 1963; Goudie, A., 1993, The human impact on the natural environment, Blackwell

about four metres in the past 140 years. Here the rate of subsidence was most rapid soon after drainage was initiated, with the installation of pumps, at the end of the last century; current rates are about 1.5 centimetres/year (Figure 3.26).

The types of sediment common to zones of subsidence include:

1 **Sand and gravel** – a loose non-coherent soil consisting of small rock and mineral particles. Gravels are different from sand, having larger particles. Layers of these materials are the source of productive aquifers, due to their high permeability. When subject to loading, their behaviour is essentially elastic.

2 **Silt** – rock fragment, mineral or debris with little or no plasticity. The silts that are not very permeable are an intermediate aggregate between sands and clay, i.e. smaller than fine sand, but larger than coarse clay.

3 **Clay** – an aggregate of microscopic particles which originated from the chemical degradation of rock components. It becomes quite plastic when a limited amount of water is present. The permeability of clay is very low.

4 **Peat** – a dark brown or black deposit produced by the decomposition and disintegration of any vegetative organic matter, such as moss and trees. It is highly compressible.

A high water table and low cohesion make undrained peat unstable. Instability increases if the area of peat continues to grow and becomes oversaturated and may lead to bog bursts. A sludgy stream rich in organic matter flows out of the bog; the bog bursts of Mayo, Kerry and Antrim in Ireland are good examples. Human activities have increased the amount of peat erosion since the early 1700s. These activities include grazing, burning, cutting, footpath erosion, military training, and

Figure 3.27 The Norfolk Broads – natural lakes or medieval peat cuttings?

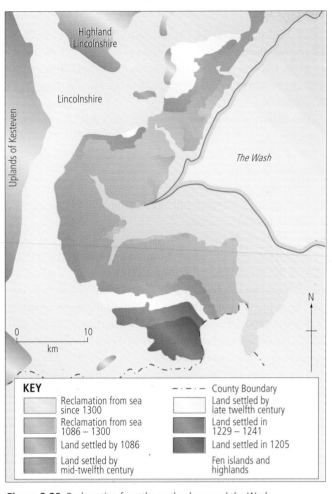

Figure 3.28 Reclamation from the wetlands around the Wash
Source: Simmons, I., 1989, Changing the face of the earth: culture, environment, history, Blackwell

increased levels of atmospheric pollution. All these activities kill the sensitive moss, and without this vegetation cover, the peaty soil is easily eroded, especially in areas of high rainfall.

One of the most intriguing of landforms is the Norfolk Broads. These are a series of lakes in the Bure, Yare and Waveney valleys. Originally it was thought that the lakes were caused by the deposition of clay and silt in the valleys, thus damming the rivers and causing lakes. Now it is believed that they are the result of peat digging, which continued until the end of the nineteenth century. Flooding of the peat works led to the formation of the Broads.

QUESTION

1 Study Figure 3.27.

a) Describe the subsidence of the Fenlands at Holme Fen Post.

b) Explain why rates of subsidence increase following drainage of the land.

RECLAMATION

Since the early mediaeval times (about 1300) land has been reclaimed from the sea. The earliest example was around the Wash. At first the amount of land reclaimed was quite small, but this increased rapidly after 1300 (Figure 3.28).

In recent decades, many holes and tips have proved to be transient features of the land surface as the demand for land-fill sites has increased. Some holes and tips have become an integral part of the leisure industry. The Broads in Norfolk and Suffolk, formed from peat diggings up to the end of the nine-teenth century, are a good example. So too are the gravel pits of the Lee Valley in Hertfordshire which now form an impor-tant water-based leisure park.

CHANGING COASTLINES

Coastlines in the UK are changing for a number of reasons:

- an increase in the amount of stormy weather
- rising sea levels
- offshore dredging
- quarrying for sand.

The problem is widespread. The Environment Agency is dredging and pumping 13 million tonnes of sand to replace sand lost from the coastline between Mablethorpe and Skegness. At Redcar, Cleveland, vanishing sands have revealed World War II fortifications, while at Burnham-on-Crouch, Essex, over 300 tonnes of sand were removed one night in 1997 due to coastal erosion.

Coasts throughout the world are the foci of human settle-ment – two-thirds of the world's population live close to the sea and half of the world's cities with populations greater than one million have a coastal location. In the UK, only in the north of Scotland do stretches of untouched coastline remain. Most coastlines are very fragile, especially those that are in wave-lashed (high energy) marine environments.

Coastal areas are subject to land reclamation. In the past many of the reclamation schemes were praised, but in recent years the damage has been highlighted. Examples include the Fenlands of England and also the Polders of the Netherlands.

Human activity is also an indirect cause of coastal erosion (Figure 3.29). One of the best illustrations of this is the abandoned fishing village of Hallsands on the south Devon coast (Figure 3.30). The village of Hallsands was destroyed in 1917 by a severe storm. The shingle beach, which had previously protected the village, had been removed by contractors building the Naval Dockyard extension at Devonport. Up to 660 000 tons of shingle were removed, lowering the beach by up to five metres. The material was not replaced by natural processes as the shingle was a relict feature deposited about 18 000 years previously by rising sea levels, and not currently being formed.

Dredging at Hallsands began in 1897 and over 1600 tons were removed daily. The shape of the beach changed and shingle was replaced in some areas by fine sand and mud. However, storms in 1902–3 removed this. In 1917 a storm destroyed all but one of the houses in the village. Contemporary writers noted that this storm was less powerful than a storm in 1891 which had inflicted relatively little damage. The impact of the storm was intensified because the shingle beach which should have protected the village had largely been removed.

Up to six metres of cliff erosion occurred between 1907 and 1957, and the area remains vulnerable to storms and wave erosion. By the mid 1990s, the cliffs at Hallsands were closed to the public owing to cliff collapse. Further along the coast, at Torcross and Beesands, artificial defences were replaced by new designs and structures in 1980 after earlier defences were overwhelmed by the storms of 1979.

Figure 3.29 *Human-induced erosion in coastal areas*
Source: Goudie, A., 1993, The human impact on the natural environment, Blackwell

Human activity	Consequences
1 Beach mining for placer deposits (sand or gravel containing tin, gold or platinum, eroded and washed down by a river)	1 Loss of sand from frontal dunes and beach ridges
2 Construction of groynes, breakwaters, jetties and other defensive structures	2 Down-drift erosion (erosion further along the coast)
3 Construction of offshore breakwaters	3 Reduction in littoral drift (drift just offshore – the littoral zone)
4 Construction of retaining walls to stabilise river entrance erosion	4 Interruption in littoral drift resulting in down-drift
5 Construction of sea walls, revetments (wooden retaining wall)	5 Wave reflection and accelerated sediment movement
6 Deforestation	6 Removal of sand by wind; sand drift
7 Fires	7 Migrating dunes and sand drift after destruction of vegetation
8 Grazing of sheep and cattle	8 Initiation of blow outs and transgressive dunes (dunes moving inland): sand drift
9 Off-road recreation vehicles (dune buggies, trail bikes)	9 Triggering mechanism for sand drift after removal of vegetation cover
10 Reclamation schemes	10 Changes in coastal configuration and interruption of natural processes, often causing new patterns of sediment transport
11 Increased recreational needs	11 Accelerated deterioration and destruction of vegetation on dunes, promoting erosion by wind and wave action

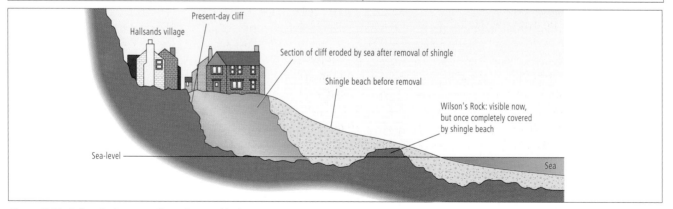

Figure 3.30 *Hallsands, Devon, a village destroyed by human activity*
Source: Nagle, G., 1998, Geography through diagrams, OUP

SUMMARY

In this chapter we have concentrated on the human modification to landforms in the UK. Some of these are the direct result of the construction and destruction of landforms, such as cuttings and embankments, whereas others are the indirect result of the modification of natural processes, for example, increased rates of weathering. There are few places which are unaffected by human activity – the most dramatic effects resulting from mining and quarrying.

QUESTIONS

1 Study Figure 3.31 which shows how land surfaces are affected by human processes.
a) Describe the impact of human activities on (i) slope stability and (ii) subsidence. Give reasons to support your answer.
b) Which of the four major human activities has the most impact? Support your answer with evidence from Figure 3.31.
c) Which human activities cause least effect or damage? Why do you think this is so?
d) Which single activity causes most impact? Justify your choice.

2 'The human impact upon the natural environment is largely negative.' Discuss this statement using examples to support your case.

EXTENDED (PROJECT) WORK

Using a CD-Rom, look up Mining, Extractive industries, Gravel works and other related terms in any of the newspapers or journals. What are the main issues that are being raised in the press? Write to some of the companies involved and ask for their annual report and/or their environmental policy. How does this compare with the information you have discovered in the newspaper articles on the CD-Rom?

BIBLIOGRAPHY AND RECOMMENDED READING

Carbognin, L., 1985, Land subsidence – A worldwide environmental hazard, *Nature and Resources*, 21, 2-12

Drew, D., 1983, *Man-environment processes*, George Allen and Unwin

Goudie, A., 1993, *The human impact on the natural environment*, 4th Edition, Blackwell

Goudie, A., 1997, *The human impact reader: readings and case studies*, Blackwell

Middleton, G., 1992, *About quarrying*, Hobson

Perry, A., 1981, *Environmental hazards in the British Isles*, George Allen and Unwin

Simmons, I., 1989, *Changing the face of the Earth: Culture, Environment, History*, Blackwell.

Wright, L., 1993, *Environmental systems and human impact*, Cambridge University Press

WEB SITES

The British Geological Society -
http://192.171.148.40/bgs/home.html
ENN Online -
http://www.enn.com/
Friends of the Earth -
http://www.foe.co.uk/
Tower Colliery -
http://www.baynet.co.uk/colliery

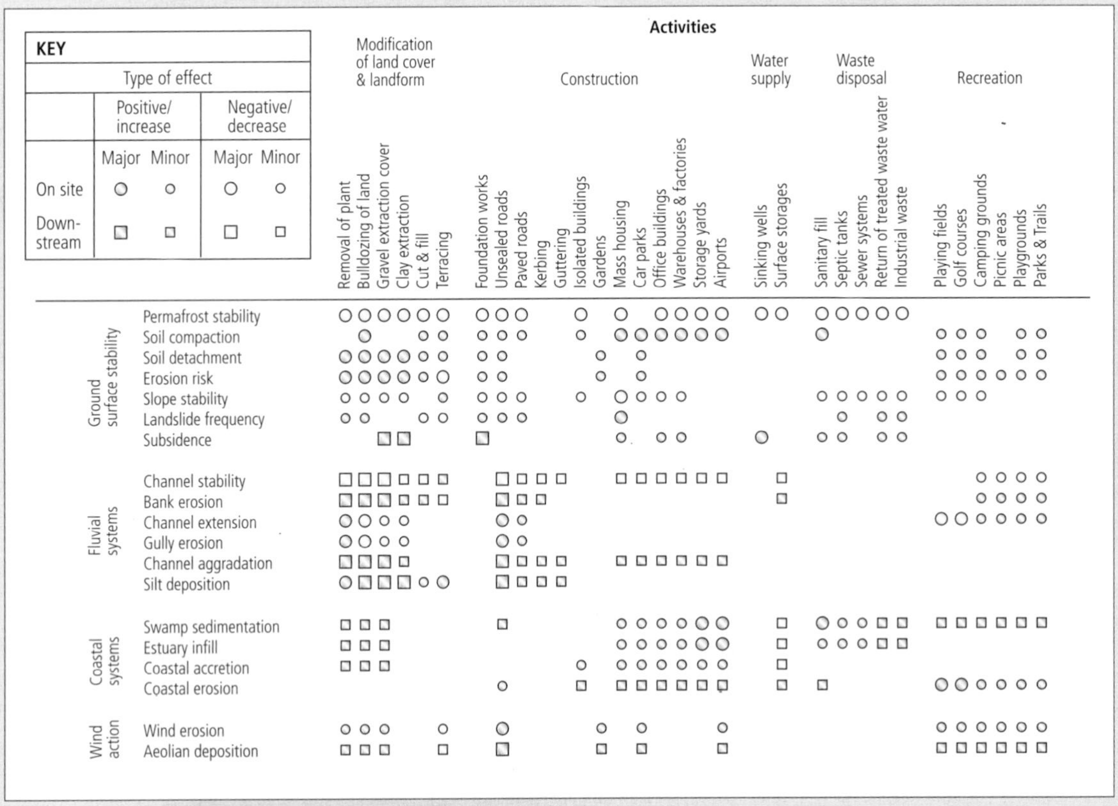

Figure 3.31 *The human impact on land surfaces*
Source: Simmons, I., 1989, *Changing the face of the earth: culture, environment, history*, Blackwell

Chapter 4
Soils

Soils are an important resource and are vital for life. Without soils, plants would be unable to grow, and human survival would be impossible. In this chapter we look at the main characteristics of soils, the ways in which they are formed, and the main types of soil in the British Isles. The second section examines the many ways in which human activity affects soils. Some methods may benefit and conserve soils, but there are many more ways in which human activities are damaging or destroying this precious resource.

WHAT ARE SOILS?

Most soils develop from the mechanical or chemical weathering of bedrock into finer particles. At the same time, rainwater containing dissolved chemicals, and acids from decomposing plants, weathers the fine particles. This releases nutrients, such as calcium, potassium and magnesium, required for plant growth. In turn, biological processes, notably the action of worms, cause further soil development, creating even finer materials and breaking down vegetation into humus. Hence, the nature of the parent material (bedrock), climate, local topography, vegetation and land-use, influence the extent of weathering and the soil type that develops (Figure 4.1). The nature and properties of soils can therefore vary significantly over relatively small areas (for instance within single fields) depending on, for example, local changes in parent material, slope and aspect.

Soil texture

Most soils are composed of sand, silt and clay which may be bound together with water and organic matter.

Sandy soils usually have weak or no structure (the soil particles are not grouped together). The spaces between the coarse particles are relatively large and allow rapid drainage of water through them. This limits the amount of water that is retained in the soil and is available for plant growth. It also increases the risk of **leaching** (downward movement of material in solution) of nitrate and pesticides out of the soil and into surface waters, especially where the soils overlie permeable rocks such as limestone and sandstone.

Soils with a high clay content have very different properties. The spaces between clay particles are much smaller than between sand particles. This greatly restricts the flow of water through it. Some clays, however, can be quite permeable as a result of cycles of shrinking and swelling, as the soils dry out and then get wet again. In these soils individ-

Figure 4.1 *A typical soil*

ual soil blocks are separated by relatively large cracks which act as drainage routes.

Clayey soils are found predominantly in the south and east of England. Under very dry summer conditions, excessive shrinkage of clay soils can cause structural damage to the houses built on them. Under average climatic conditions, clay shrinkage is not a major problem, but in the major dry periods, such as 1971 to 1976, 1984 and in the 1990s, extensive damage from subsidence has been caused. Increasingly dry years may result in greater damage.

Silty soils, particularly those with low organic matter content, often have a very weak structure and are susceptible to waterlogging or saturation. This can restrict seedling germination, and increase the risk of erosion. The physical and chemical properties of loamy soils (mixed soils) depends on the relative proportions of sand, silt and clay.

Soil structure

Soil structure refers to the shape of the individual soil particles or peds and their grouping. Due to cementing by chemicals, such as calcium, iron, aluminium and quartz, in the soil, individual particles will often aggregate in lumps. A crumb structure rather like grains of rounded sound (Figure 4.3, see page 68) is probably the best for agriculture, as it allows water and air into the soil, whereas a prismatic structure (often the result of clay particles sticking together) inhibits the free movement of water and air. Structure can be improved through ploughing and turning over the soil, and/or adding organic matter or humus.

Skills:
Triangular graphs

Texture
Sand   0.2–2 mm
Silt   0.02–0.2 mm
Clay   ≤ 0.02 mm

Triangular graphs are used to show three sets of data each of which can be divided into three types, e.g. soil (sand, silt and clay), employment (primary, secondary and tertiary), and population (young, adult and elderly). The data need to be in percentages totalling 100%. The main advantages of triangular graphs are that they allow:

- a large number of data to be shown on one graph (think how many pie charts or bar charts would be used to show all the data on Figure 4.2)
- groupings to be easily recognisable – in the case of soils, groups of soil texture can be identified
- dominant characteristics to be shown easily
- classifications to be drawn up.

The method of plotting a soil is shown on Figure 4.2.

Figure 4.2 *Triangular graphs*
Source: Nagle, G. and Spencer, K., 1997,
Geographical enquiries, Stanley Thornes

QUESTIONS

1   Identify the clay, silt and sand content of the following soils: A, B, C, and D.
2   Plot:
(i)   clay 30%, sand 45% and silt 25%
(ii) clay 50%, sand 30% and silt 20%
(iii) clay 20%, sand 35% and silt 45%
(iv) clay 37%, sand 36% and silt 27%.

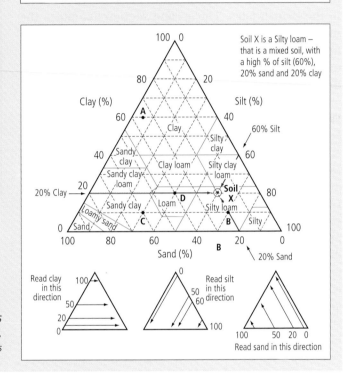

Soil X is a Silty loam – that is a mixed soil, with a high % of silt (60%), 20% sand and 20% clay

Soil moisture

The amount of water in a soil depends on a number of factors including texture, organic matter content and soil density. During winter, soils take in water until they reach a state known as field capacity. Where soils are free draining, any excess water drains through the soil. By contrast, impeded drainage results in waterlogging or saturation. When the loss of water by plant uptake and evaporation is greater than rainfall the soil begins to dry out. The soil moisture deficit that develops is measured as the amount of rainfall required to return the soil to field capacity (Figure 4.4).

Soil nutrients

Nutrients include all trace elements and minerals within the soil. Sources of nutrients and their availability vary, and involve complex interactions within the soil. Nitrogen and sulphur are naturally derived from the breakdown of soil organic matter and inputs from acidic deposition. Elements

Figure 4.3 *Soil structure*
Source: Goudie, A., 1994, The encyclopaedic dictionary of physical geography, Blackwell

such as phosphorus, potassium and calcium are predominantly provided by the weathering of soil particles or parent material.

Soil nutrients or minerals are sometimes called bases. Base exchange, or cation exchange, is the process whereby bases such as calcium, magnesium, and sodium are made available to plants. Plants use bases for growth and therefore take them from the soil (and some of them from the atmosphere). In return, plants provide the soil with hydrogen ions. This makes the soil more acid (acidity is a measure of the level of exchangeable hydrogen present). However, nutrients may be returned to the soil by leaf fall, the use of fertilisers and the weathering of rocks. The **cation exchange capacity** of the soil is the capacity of the soil to retain positively charged chemicals. A soil with a high cation exchange capacity is more fertile than a soil with a low cation exchange capacity because it provides plants with more nutrients than a soil with a low cation exchange capacity (Figure 4.5).

Soil horizons

Soil horizons are layers within a soil (Figure 4.6). They vary in texture, structure, colour, acidity (pH) and mineral content.

The top layer of soil is referred to as the organic (O) horizon.

Beneath this is the mixed mineral-organic layer (A horizon). It is generally a dark colour due to the presence of organic matter. An Ap horizon is one mixed by ploughing.

In some soils there are very distinct layers, for example, a podzol or a rendzina. These reflect the downward movement of materials and/or the influence of geology (as in a rendzina). However, in a ploughed soil, all the upper layers are mixed. An Ah horizon contains proportionately more humus than other A horizons.

In some soils leaching takes place, removing material from the eluvial (E) horizon which becomes much lighter in colour than the A horizon. In a podzol, where leaching is intense, an ash-coloured Ea horizon is formed. By contrast, in a brown earth, where leaching is less intense, a light brown Eb horizon is found.

The B horizon is the deposited or illuvial horizon. This horizon contains material such as iron (fe), humus (h) and clay (t) that has been moved from the E horizon. Sometimes the B horizon is weathered (w).

At the base of the horizons is the parent material or bedrock (C). Sometimes labels are given to distinguish solid rock (r) from unconsolidated loose deposits (u).

QUESTIONS

1 Identify the following horizons: **(i)** Bfe, **(ii)** Ap, **(iii)** Cu and **(iv)** Ea.

2 What abbreviations would you give for **(i)** a deposited horizon containing humus, **(ii)** a slightly leached horizon, **(iii)** a waterlogged organic horizon?

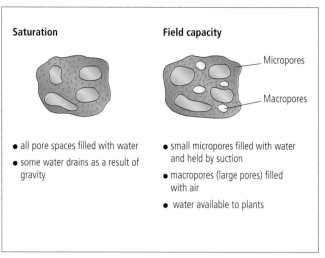

Figure 4.4 *Soil moisture*
Source: Nagle, G. and Spencer, K.,1997, Advanced geography revision handbook, OUP

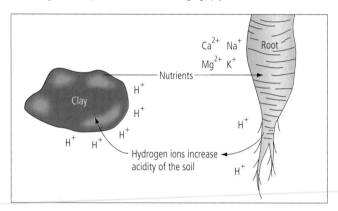

Figure 4.5 *Soil chemistry*
Source: Nagle, G. and Spencer, K.,1997, Advanced geography revision handbook, OUP

O organic horizon
l   undecomposed litter
f   partly decomposed (fermenting) litter
h   well decomposed humus (decomposed plant remains)

A mixed mineral-organic horizon
h   humus
p   ploughed, as in a field or a garden
g   gleyed or waterlogged

E eluvial or leached horizon
a   strongly leached, ash coloured horizon, as in a podzol
b   weakly leached, light brown horizon, as in a brown earth

B illuvial or deposited horizon
fe iron deposited
t   clay deposited
h   humus deposited

C bedrock or parent material
r   rock
u   unconsolidated
w   weathered

Figure 4.6 *Soil horizons*

FACTORS AFFECTING SOIL FORMATION

Many factors, such as parent material (geology), climate, biota (flora and fauna), topography (relief), human activities and time, influence soil development.

Geology

There is a widespread misunderstanding that parent material (bedrock) determines soil type. In general, the main global soil groups do not accord with geology.

Parent material has an effect on texture, structure and fertility: sandstones and gritstones produce free draining, coarse textured soils, whereas clays and shales give much finer soils. Soil fertility is also affected by the bedrock – the initial nutrients and bases are provided by weathering of the bedrock. These nutrients and bases may be removed or added to at a later stage by various geomorphological processes, such as overland run-off, river erosion or deposition.

The distinction between calcareous and non-calcareous rocks is very important for soil fertility. Calcareous rocks, such as chalk and limestone, are base rich (rich in positively charged nutrients) whereas others, such as granite and sandstone, tend to be acidic, lacking chemicals such as calcium, magnesium, sodium and potassium, and often give rise to acidic podzolic soils. Figure 4.7 shows a rendzina soil – a thin soil developed on chalk or limestone.

Climate

Two major climatic influences operate on soils – temperature and precipitation (Figure 4.8). Temperature affects the rate of chemical and biological reactions. Van't Hoff's law states that the rate of chemical weathering increases two to three times for every increase in temperature of 10°C. In cool climates bacterial action is relatively slow and a thick layer of decomposing vegetation often covers the ground. By con-

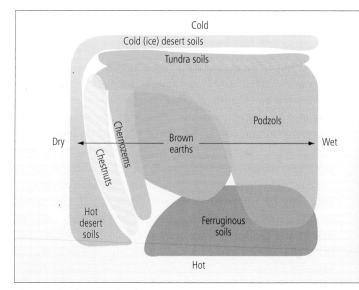

Figure 4.8 *Climate and soils*
Source: Nagle. G. and Spencer, K., 1997 Advanced geography revision handbook, OUP

trast, in the humid tropics, bacteria thrive and, although leaf fall is great, the vegetation is rapidly decomposed and translocated down the soil profile, through rapid leaching in the very wet conditions.

Precipitation (PPT) is important in relation to potential evapotranspiration (pEVT). The process of leaching depends upon whether PPT > pEVT, and by how much. Where PPT > pEVT, the removal of free calcium in the soil by leaching, leaves behind aluminium and iron oxides, normally deposited at depth (usually 60 – 100 cm) within the soil. Any soil in which there is a net downward movement through the soil is known as a **pedalfer**. By contrast, if pEVT > PPT there is a soil water deficit and water is drawn to the evaporating surface, bringing with it calcium carbonate. Such soils are known as **pedocals** and are typical of arid and semi-arid environments.

Biotic factors

Organic matter is a basic component of soil, although the influences of biotic (living) factors range from microscopic creatures to man. Some influences are indirect, such as interception of PPT by vegetation and the reduction of PPT via EVT. Others are direct, such as the release of humic (organic) acids by decaying vegetation or the return of nutrients to the soil via litter decay.

Animals, too, have an effect on soils. In the top 30 centimetres of one hectare of soil there are on average twenty five tonnes of soil organisms, consisting of:

- ten tonnes of bacteria
- ten tonnes of fungi
- four tonnes of earthworms
- one tonne of other soil organisms such as mites (for example, spring tails and isopods), spiders, snails and mice.

Figure 4.7 *A rendzina soil*

Earthworms alone can represent from 50–70% of the total weight of creatures in arable soils. In one hectare, 18–40 tonnes of soil is ingested each day by earthworms and passed on to the surface. This represents a layer up to five millimetres deep. Human activity has obvious effects, ranging from liming (to neutralise adic soils), fertiliser application and mulching (putting straw/hay on the soil surface to reduce wind erosion and raise soil temperature) to mining, deforestation, agricultural practices and extraction of peat for gardening purposes. These are considered in detail on pages 78–82.

Topography

Slope angle affects the susceptibility of soil to erosion. In addition, steeper slopes are associated with thinner soils. Situation is also important: on a flat hill top, material is exposed to denudation processes such as erosion, weathering and man movement, whereas on a flat lowland, existing material is likely to be buried by deposition. Soils on hillsides tend to be better drained, whereas those in valley bottoms are subject to gleying (waterlogging). The direction in which a slope faces, aspect, has an important bearing on soil formation, as it affects the local climate or micro-climate.

A **catena** is the variation in soils along a slope owing to changes in relief, micro-climate (temperature, wind, PPT, EVT), drainage and the position of the water table, although the bedrock remains the same (Figure 4.9). Such a sequence can be found when following a transect from a mountain or hill top to the valley bottom.

Time

Time is not a causative factor. It does not cause soils to change, but it does allow other processes to operate to a greater extent, therefore allowing soils to evolve. The amount of time required for soil formation varies from soil to soil. A coarse sandstone bedrock develops soils more quickly than granites or basalts, and on glacial outwash a few hundred years may be enough for a soil to evolve. Thin soils are not necessarily young soils, nor are deep ones 'mature'. Phases of erosion and deposition keep some soils always in a state of evolution. Most temperate soils are referred to as polycyclic, that is, they undergo frequent changes as the major soil forming processes change, in relation to changing inputs.

SOIL CLASSIFICATIONS

The **zonal** classification of soils states that soils are determined by climatic factor (Figure 4.10). On a global scale, a map of world climates and a map of world soils bear a strong resemblance to each other. Indeed, on a general scale this is the case, with brown earths in temperate climates, podzols in cool temperate climates and chernozems (black earths in dry grassland areas) in continental climates.

The **intrazonal** classification states that within any climate belt, soils vary with respect to local factors such as geology. Certainly this is the case with limestone and chalk which give rise to rendzina soils. A good example is the Isle of Purbeck where the geological sequence of limestone, clay, chalk and glacial sands and gravels corresponds to rendzinas, brown earths or gleys, rendzinas and podzols respectively (Figure 4.13, see page 73).

The **azonal** classification states that many soils are young or immature so that there has not been sufficient time for them to develop the characteristics that would relate them to either bedrock or climate.

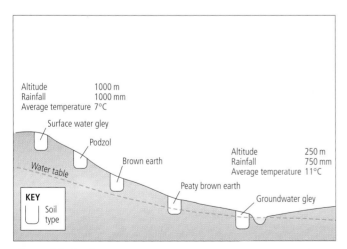

Figure 4.9 A soil catena
Source: Nagle, G. and Spencer, K.,1997, Advanced geography revision handbook, OUP

1 Zonal soils

Climatic region	Vegetation zone	Zonal soil
tundra	tundra arctic	brown soil
boreal	coniferous forest	podzol
temperate	oceanic deciduous/mixed	brown earth forest
Mediterranean	Mediterranean forest	red brown earth
mid-latitude	continental steppe/prairie	chernozem
semi-arid	semi-arid	sierozem
arid	arid	no true soil
equatorial	rainforest	latosols

2 Intrazonal soils

Modifying factor	Example of intrazonal soil
parent material	rendzina (limestone)
excess water	gley
excess salt	solonchak/solentz

3 Azonal soils

Cause of immaturity	Example of specific soil
high altitudes (low temperatures)	lithosols
inhibited decay of organic matter	peat (histosol)

Figure 4.10 Climatic regions, vegetation zones and major soil types
Source: Drew, D., 1984, Man-environment processes, Oliver and Boyd

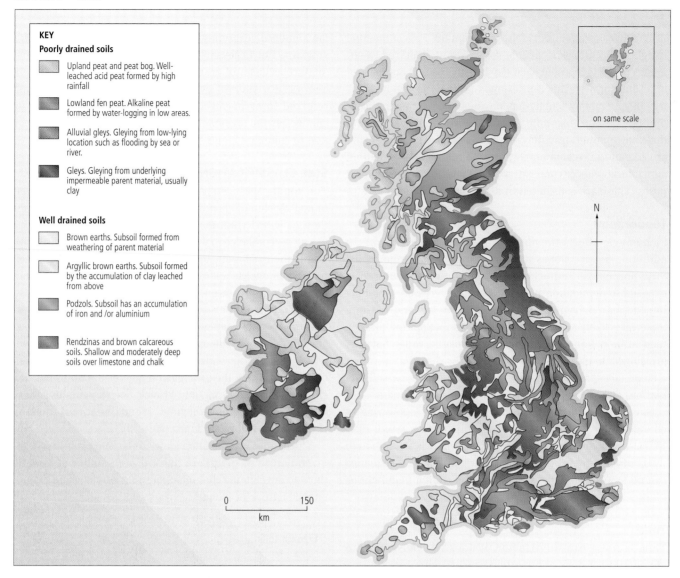

KEY

Poorly drained soils

Upland peat and peat bog. Well-leached acid peat formed by high rainfall

Lowland fen peat. Alkaline peat formed by water-logging in low areas.

Alluvial gleys. Gleying from low-lying location such as flooding by sea or river.

Gleys. Gleying from underlying impermeable parent material, usually clay

Well drained soils

Brown earths. Subsoil formed from weathering of parent material

Argyllic brown earths. Subsoil formed by the accumulation of clay leached from above

Podzols. Subsoil has an accumulation of iron and /or aluminium

Rendzinas and brown calcareous soils. Shallow and moderately deep soils over limestone and chalk

on same scale

0 — 150 km

Figure 4.11 *Soils in the UK*
Source: Goudie, A., and Brunsden, D., 1994, The environment of the British Isles, an atlas, OUP

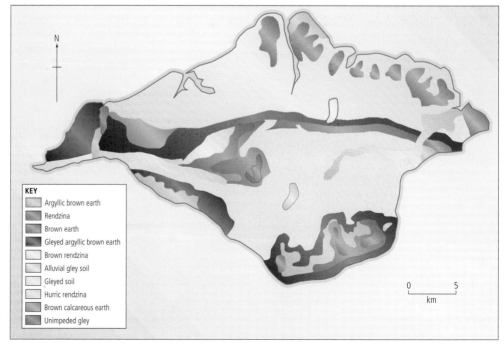

KEY

Argyllic brown earth

Rendzina

Brown earth

Gleyed argyllic brown earth

Brown rendzina

Alluvial gley soil

Gleyed soil

Hurric rendzina

Brown calcareous earth

Unimpeded gley

0 — 5 km

Figure 4.12 *Soils on the Isle of Wight*
Source: Redrawn from Soils of south east England, 1983, Ordnance Survey

SOIL FORMING PROCESSES

Soil forming processes are complex and include:
- gains and losses of material to the profile
- movement of water between the horizons
- chemical transformations within each individual horizon.

Soils must be considered as open systems in a state of dynamic equilibrium. This means they vary constantly as the factors and processes that influence them change.

The main processes include translocation, organic changes, gleying and podzolisation. In addition, the weathering of bedrock gives the soil its C horizon, as well as its initial bases and nutrients (fertility), structure and texture (drainage).

Translocation

Translocation includes many processes, mostly by water, and mostly downwards (Figure 4.14). Where PPT > pEVT, **leaching** (the downward movement of material in solution) and **eluviation** (the moving of small particles, such as clay and humus down the soil) occur. The parallel between these processes and solution and suspension in a river is clear. These movements produce eluvial (removal) and illuvial (deposited) horizons.

GEOLOGY

Geology has a lasting effect on soils through **texture**, **structure** and **fertility**. Sandstones produce free-draining soils whereas clays and shales give much finer soils. The distinction between calcerous rocks, e.g. chalk, which are base-rich or basic, and non-calcareous rocks, e.g. granite, which are base-poor or acidic, is important. On a regional scale soils often vary with geology, as in the case of the Isle of Purbeck.

The **intrazonal** classification states that within a climatic zone soils vary with rock type.

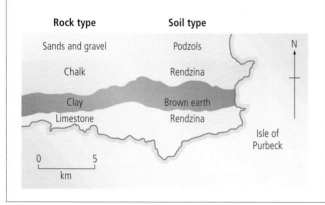

Figure 4.13 Soils and geology on the Isle of Purbeck
Source: Nagle, G. and Spencer, K., 1997, Advanced geography revision handbook, OUP

In dry environments where pEVT > PPT the movement of solutions is upwards through the soil. Water is drawn to the surface by capillary action and leaching is generally ineffective apart from occasional storms. Calcium carbonates and other solutes therefore remain in the soil. This process is known as **calcification**. In grasslands, calcification is enhanced because grasses require calcium, drawing it up from lower layers and returning it to the upper layers when they die. It is possible that Britain will experience increased rates of calcification over forthcoming decades as a result of global warming (see pages 22-27).

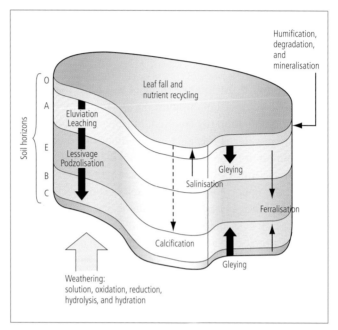

Figure 4.14 Translocation
Source: Nagle, G. and Spencer, K., 1997, Advanced geography revision handbook, OUP

QUESTION

1 Study Figure 4.12 which shows soils and geology on the Isle of Wight.

a) Identify the soils found at A, B and C.

b) Draw a soil profile to show a rendzina and a gley soil.

c) Describe the distribution of rendzina soils on the Isle of Wight.

d) How do you explain the pattern of rendzina soils?

e) What effects do the rivers have on the type of soil found?

Organic changes

Organic changes in a soil mostly occur at or near the surface. Plant litter is humified (decomposed) into a dark shapeless mass. It is also degraded gradually by fungi, algae, small insects, bacteria and worms. Under very wet conditions, humification creates peat. Over a long time scale, humus decomposes due to mineralisation, which releases nitrogenous compounds. Degradation, humification and mineralisation are not separable processes and always accompany each other.

Gleying

Gleying means waterlogging. Wet or waterlogged areas produce anaerobic (oxygen deficient) conditions, which favour the growth of specialised bacteria. These bacteria reduce ferric iron to a soluble ferrous state in a process known as **reduction**. Gley soils are characterised by a thick compact layer of sticky, structureless clay. Blue-grey blotches indicate the presence of reduced iron (red or brown blotches suggest oxidised iron, and are associated with periodic drying out of the soil). Gley soils are generally found below the water table (the top of the level of the saturated bedrock) or in areas of poor drainage.

Podzolisation

Podzolisation is an intense form of leaching that occurs under acidic conditions (Figure 4.15). Acid water leaches iron and aluminium. (By contrast, in tropical rainforests the percolating water is less acid, and so does not remove iron and aluminium.) Due to differential solubility (iron and aluminium are more soluble in acid water than for example quartz), the upper horizons of the soil become rich in silica and are a characteristic ash-grey colour. The illuvial horizon becomes rich in sesquioxides, especially iron and aluminium. This may even cause an iron pan, a thin tough horizon of iron oxides. The cause of this translocation is the leaching of certain humic acids, called **chelating agents**. This makes the water more acidic and it is able to remove iron and aluminium in solution. Heath plants and coniferous vegetation contain high levels of these acids (grasses and deciduous vegetation growing in base rich (nutrient rich) conditions have low levels of these acids) and podzols are thus generally associated with coniferous or heathland vegetation.

QUESTIONS

1 Define the following terms: leaching, podzolisation, gleying.

2 Study Figure 4.15.

a) Describe the process of podzolisation. What materials are being removed? Why does this happen? Where are they being redeposited?

MAIN SOIL TYPES IN BRITAIN

This section looks at the main soil types in Britain (Figure 4.11, see page 72). There are 'ideal' or model soils, and in many cases they merge, for example there are podzolised brown earths, gleyed brown earths, gleyed podzols, and so on.

Podzols

Podzols are highly leached soils (Figure 4.16). They occur where the soil is sandy and where leaching is intense. They contain a raw, acidic humus (pH 4.5-5.5) and have a bleached horizon, caused by the removal of iron, aluminium and organic matter from the upper layers of the soil.

Podzols are one of the most distinct soil types, related to very specific conditions (Figure 4.17). They are found under coniferous vegetation and heathlands, and climatically, they are associated with cool temperate regions. These areas have a low annual precipitation (500-800 millimetres), low winter temperatures (< 0°C) and summer temperatures over 10°C. Rapid leaching may occur in spring due to fast snowmelt. Podzols are found in highland areas of granite and sandstone (acid rocks). Under heathlands, permeable sands and gravels allow the free movement of water downwards.

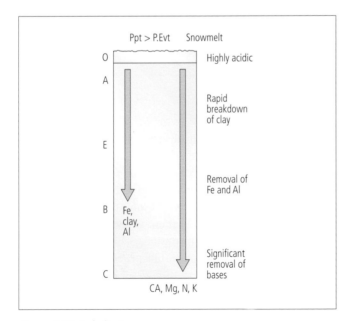

Figure 4.15 Podzolisation
Source: Nagle, G. and Spencer, K., 1997, Advanced geography revision handbook, OUP

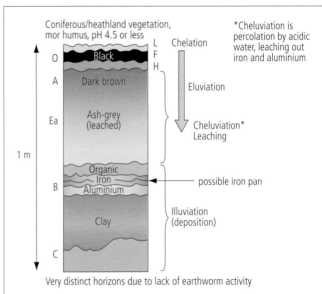

Figure 4.16 Podzols
Source: Nagle, G. and Spencer, K., 1997, Advanced geography revision handbook, OUP

Heather and coniferous vegetation release few bases (positive ions). Instead they release humic acids, called chelating agents. These allow iron and aluminium to be carried in solution (leached) down through the profile and deposited in the B horizon. Clay and humus may be carried in suspension by the percolating water (eluviation). This leads to the relative accumulation of silica in the upper horizons, giving the soil its characteristic bleached, ash-grey E horizon. The upper O and A horizons are black, owing to the presence of a very raw, acidic humus called **mor**; the thick, waxy, acidic needles of coniferous trees do not break down easily, leading to the thick accumulation of humus on podzols. The B horizon is also dark, reflecting the presence of deposited clay and humus. Under intense conditions an impermeable iron pan may be formed. The C horizon can be up to 1 metre thick, and tends to take on the colour of the underlying bedrock.

The horizons tend to be quite distinct, due to the acidic nature of the soil, which limits the presence of earthworms, one of the main horizon-mixers.

Brown earths

Brown earths are freely or moderately well drained soils (Figure 4.18). They occur in warm temperate climate zones where PPT > pEVT, thereby allowing the downward movement of particles through the soil (Figure 4.19). Brown earths are the main soils in the British Isles. For example, around Oxford annual precipitation is about 750 millimetres and pEVT around 650 millimetres; summer

Figure 4.18 *A typical brown earth – note the transition from dark brown to light brown and the lack of distinct horizons*

temperatures reach about 18°C, and winter temperatures 5–7°C. The main type of natural vegetation is temperate broad-leafed deciduous forest.

At the surface, the annual shedding of leaves conserves nutrients and the humus that develops is mildly acidic with pH 5.5–6.5; it is called **mull**. A mull humus is a fertile humus with a crumb structure. The upper horizons are dark brown. The B horizon is light brown owing to the removal of clay and humus by eluviation and iron and aluminium by leaching. The process of leaching is less strong than in a podzol and so the horizon is not as bleached. Soil fauna, such as worms, springtails and isopods flourish, consequently horizons are mixed. The soil is relatively fertile and may be up to one metre thick, excluding the C horizon. Some brown earths may contain redeposited layers of clay taken from the E horizon, and are termed **argillic** (clay rich) brown earths.

Figure 4.17 *A typical podzol*

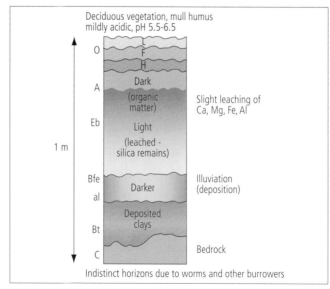

Figure 4.19 *Brown earth*

Source: Nagle, G. and Spencer, K., 1997, Advanced geography revision handbook, OUP

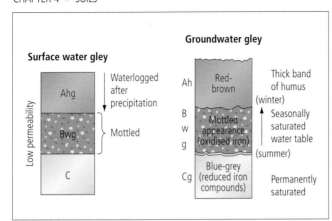

Figure 4.20 *Gleyed soils*
Source: Nagle, G., and Spencer, K., 1997, Advanced geography revision handbook, OUP

Gleyed soils

Gleyed soils are waterlogged or saturated soils. The colour varies from red to grey to brown and may even be speckled, depending upon whether the iron has been reduced or oxidised. Two main types of gley soils occur (Figure 4.20):

- surface water gleys, in areas of low permeability where rain water is collected on the surface
- ground water gleys where the waterlogging is caused by a high water table.

The transition between the gleyed horizons and the freely drained horizons is marked by a zone of mottling, in which there is periodic waterlogging and drying out. Gley soils are mottled (blotchy) because the soil pores are filled with water containing dissolved organic substances. The suffix 'g' is used to denote a gleyed horizon.

Gleyed soils are associated with upland peats and moors and with lowland fens. Acid upland peats and peat bogs are found in the higher, wetter and cooler parts of western Britain. Here, severe leaching is common. Due to low temperatures, biological activity is reduced, and there is a slower breakdown of plant material than in the Fens. By contrast, lowland fen peat occurs in waterlogged areas at lower altitude, such as the Fens of East Anglia. These are more alkaline than their upland counterparts, because they contain chalk.

Chernozem

Chernozems are associated with continental temperate climates, such as the Steppes of Russia or the Great Plains of North America. There is an upward movement of water through the soil because pEVT > PPT. Hence the soil is a pedocal. Chernozems are also referred to as black earths, owing to the accumulation of organic matter throughout the soil. They are found on prairie grasslands, for example bluestem grass, up to 2.5 metres high, and little bluestem, up to 1.5 metres high. The soil is alkaline and has a good crumb structure (owing to the humus), which makes it highly suitable for agriculture. The thickly matted root system, up to 1 metre deep, reduces the risk of soil erosion. The

dominant process is the upward movement of water to the drying surface. Grasses also draw up calcium, thus there is the accumulation of bases at the surface. Often there are no B or E horizons, because there is limited downward movement. Some leaching does occur, associated with snowmelt in spring and periodic thunderstorms during the late summer.

Although chernozem soils are not usually associated with the British Isles, global warming could lead to an increase in temperatures in the south and east of England sufficient to produce consistent water shortages in the summer.

Rendzina

Rendzinas are soils which develop on chalk or limestone (Figure 4.8, see page 70). They consist of a single organic horizon which is rich in calcium (pH 7.0-pH 8.0) and rests on bedrock (Figure 4.21). The upper horizon is black or brown, indicating a soil rich in organic matter; it is thin (often only 5–10 millimetres). Below this is the C horizon. At the top of the C horizon there may be angular fragments. These originate from a time when mechanical weathering was frequent on chalk and limestone, such as during a periglacial period. Beneath this is pure bedrock. Rendzina soils are examples of intrazonal soils – that is, those developed on a particular rock type, rather than due to climatic conditions. They are found on chalk and limestone. If the bedrock contains many impurities, such as flint or chert on chalk, or magnesium or iron on limestone, these minerals could form the basis of B and E horizons.

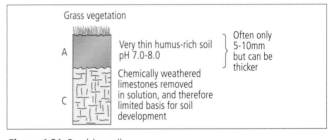

Figure 4.21 *Rendzina soil*
Source: Nagle, G., and Spencer, K., 1997, Advanced geography revision handbook, OUP

QUESTIONS

1 Study Figure 4.22 which shows some soils in southern England.

a) Identify each of the soil types A, B and C.

b) Explain how they have been formed.

2

a) Label the four soils A, B, C, D, on Figure 4.23 choosing from: podzols; brown earth; ground water gley and peat soil.

b) Explain why the soils at A and B differ in terms of leaching. How and why do environmental conditions vary between A and B?

c) Compare the soils at C and D. Why is the amount of organic matter much thicker at D?

d) Why is there a mottled zone in soil C? How is this caused?

e) Which site offers the best potential for agriculture? Explain your choice.

f) Which site offers the least potential for agriculture? Explain your choice.

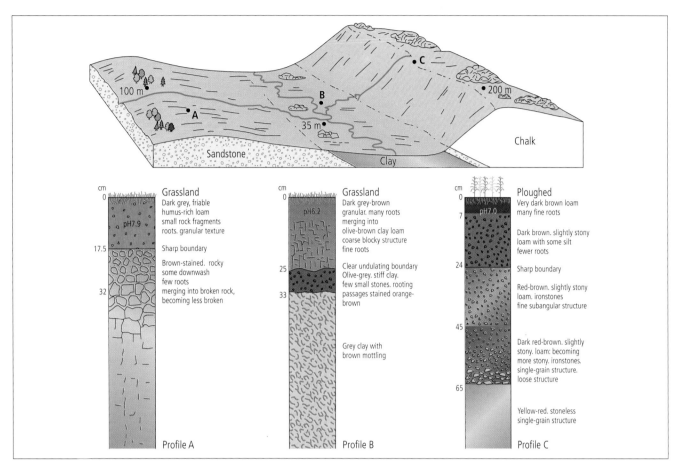

Figure 4.22 *Soils in southern Britain*
Source: University of Oxford, Delegacy of Local Examinations, 1988 (A-level question)

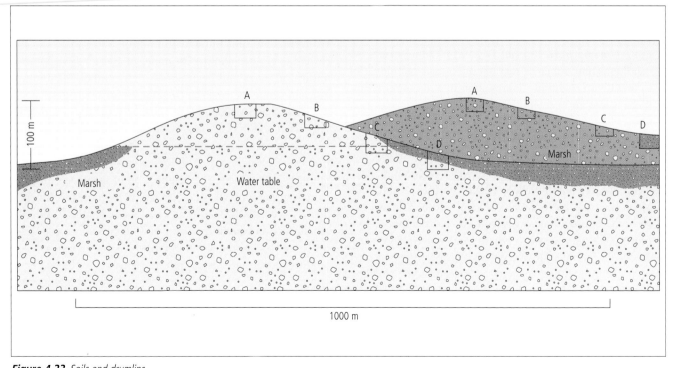

Figure 4.23 *Soils and drumlins*
Source: Nagle, G. and Spencer, K., 1996, Investigating Geography Hodder and Stoughton

Urban soils

In urban areas much soil is covered by buildings and roads and is also compacted under footpaths (Figure 4.24). Only in open parks and gardens is soil left uncovered. Soil in urban areas differs from soil in rural areas in a number of ways:

- **Mineral content** – In many urban areas, the predominant minerals found in new soil (less than 150 years old) come from the disintegrating cement of walls and the remains of weathering of brick and concrete. These and other building materials have a high calcium content (often formed from limestone) so the plants which thrive in these soils are those which can tolerate a high calcium content. These are known as **calcicole** plants.

- **pH** – Walls have a high pH because cement used in the mortar is made of Portland limestone, although in time many of the calcium salts leach out of the mortar. The pH of garden soil is usually determined by the rock on which it is formed, however, as many gardens contain building rubble in the sub-strata underneath the soil, many urban soils tends to be alkaline.

- **Nutrients** – In many urban areas the main sources of organic matter which could decompose to become humus are fallen leaves, human litter, bird droppings and dog excrement. However, these are very often cleaned from streets and parks so the nutrients are removed before they can be broken down and returned to the soil. In formal parkland gardens, dead plants, fallen leaves and cuttings are removed, although they may be used as compost. Alternatively, nutrients may be replaced by artificial fertilisers.

- **Water conditions** – Water conditions in urban areas vary quite considerably. Run-off is great in some areas, so conditions may either be very dry or compaction may lead to local waterlogging. Compaction of soils means that there is less air space in the soil.

THE EFFECT OF HUMAN ACTIVITY

The human impact on soils is extensive (Figure 4.25). The main effect is to create artificial soils at a regional or local level. These are sometimes described as **intrazonal** soils because they are variations of the soil within a broad climatic zone. For example, we have seen that the main zonal soil for the UK is a brown earth, but in some upland areas podzols are found, many of which are the result of past episodes of human activity, such as deforestation, burning and grazing.

The main threats to soil quality and quantity include:
- acidification
- accumulation of pollutants and heavy metals
- organic matter loss, deteriorating soil structure and associated problems

Figure 4.24 *Urban soil*
Source: Nagle, G., and Spencer, K., 1997, Advanced geography revision handbook, OUP

- nitrates and phosphates in water resources
- organic contaminants in water resources
- increasing urban areas, road building and industrial developments
- erosion.

Acidification

We have seen that the distribution of acid soils is closely related to climate and parent material. Soil acidification is a natural process and in areas of high rainfall, leaching of nutrient elements from the soil leads to increasing soil acidity. Thus, acid soils dominate large areas of the UK, that is, they are found in clay areas with peaty soils and a high percentage of exchangeable hydrogen, especially upland areas. However, human activities can accelerate the process. Changes in land use, the application of fertilisers and the increased amounts of acidic precipitation have been identified as potentially major threats to soil fertility and soil structure, and leaching of iron and aluminium in soils into water, causing acidification of lakes.

Most of the podzols in upland Britain are the result of human activity. In particular, deforestation, burning and farming have led to an increase in leaching, and acidic and podzolised conditions. A number of stages can be observed:

- deforestation limits the return of nutrients to the soil; many of these nutrients were taken from the lower layers of the soil during tree growth, and returned to the upper layers through leaf fall

Soil factor	Beneficial change	Neutral change	Adverse change
soil chemistry	mineral fertilisers (increased fertility) add trace elements desalinise (irrigation) increase oxidation (aeration)	alter exchangeable ion balance alter pH (lime) alter via vegetation changes	chemical imbalance toxic herbicides and herbicides salinise over-removal of nutrients
soil physics	increase crumb structure (lime and grass) maintain texture (organic manure or conditioner) deep ploughing, alter soil moisture (irrigation or drainage)	alter structure (ploughing, harrowing) alter soil microclimate (mulches, shelter belts, heating, albedo change)	compaction/plough pan (poor structure) adverse structure due to chemical changes (salts) remove perennial vegetation
soil organisms	organic manure increase pH drain/moisten aerate	alter vegetation and soil microclimate	remove vegetation and plough (less worms and micro-organisms) pathogens, e.g. slurry toxic chemicals
time (rate of change)	rejuvenate (deep ploughing, adding new soil, reclaiming land)		accelerated erosion overuse of nutrients urbanise land

Figure 4.25 *Some effects of human activity on soil characteristics*
Source: Drew, D., 1984, Man-environment processes, George Allen and Unwin

- burning releases a number of nutrients in the soil (see Inset 4.1 on Fire and soil, page 80)
- cultivation of crops extracts nutrients from the soil which may not be replenished by manure or fertilisers
- invading plant species, notably bracken and heather, produce a more acidic humus, intensifying the soil's acidity.

In turn, podzols may lead to the development of peat bogs, which are even less cultivable. This is partly due to the development of iron pans in podzols, which hinder the downward flow of water causing the waterlogged conditions in which peat may form. In addition, with less forest cover, there is reduced interception of rainfall by foliage; with more water reaching the soil, waterlogging may occur. In the UK, the formation of many peat bogs coincides with major upland clearances in the past.

Increasing acidity in soils is thought to be a contributory factor to forest decline in central Europe, although there is little clear evidence of this in the UK. Increased acidity also has the effect of increasing the solubility of metals in the soil, including aluminium, lead, cadmium and zinc. This increases the risk of leaching into, and contamination of, surface and groundwater.

Heavy metal contamination

Soil contamination by heavy metals can originate from a number of sources, including geological parent material, industrial processes (metal-based industries, the burning of fossil fuels, waste incineration, chemical industries and the use of leaded petrol) and farming practices (applications of sewage sludge, farm wastes and fertilisers).

Disposal of sewage sludge on land has proved a significant source of heavy metal contamination in some soils, because the sludge can contain heavy metals, for example arsenic, lead, zinc and copper. Levels of these heavy metals, however, are generally higher in urban and industrial areas. Once in a soil, many heavy metals bind to organic matter or clays and are largely unavailable to plants. However, the availability of most metals increases as a soil becomes more acid, increasing the risk to plants and animals through uptake, and metal leaching into surface or groundwater under extreme conditions.

Pesticides and weedkillers

Pesticides and weedkillers (organic solvents) can affect a soil directly by:

- adsorption onto clays and organic matter (in adsorption, films of water surround individual particles of soil, and pesticides and weedkillers can get into these films of water)
- affecting soil microorganisms and plant growth
- being transported through the soil to surface and groundwater and thereby affecting drinking water supplies.

Pesticides and weedkillers are not only used in agriculture. The control of weeds along railways, motorways, footpaths and amenity areas, for example, has been identified as a significant source of polluted run-off. Many of these areas are adjacent to artificial drainage systems, leading to direct contamination of surface and groundwater. The risk of leaching of nitrate and pesticides into aquifers is greatest on shallow or sandy soils particularly where they overlie permeable rocks.

Inset 4.1
Fire and soil

Fire releases nutrients by breaking down the cell structure of organic matter. The organic matter is released as carbon dioxide and water while the nutrients, such as phosphorus (P), magnesium (Mg), potassium (K) and calcium (Ca), are returned to the soil. Soil acidity may change: the released phosphates are acidic although this may be balanced, in part, by the release of calcium. Following burning, nutrients may be lost through wind erosion or run-off. However, if pyrophytic vegetation (vegetation that is adapted to fire) is burnt, seeds will germinate, leading to plant growth which will retain the nutrients.

In the British Isles, fire occurs regularly in a number of places:

- on sand dunes as a result of barbeques and bonfires going out of control
- on farms as a result of stubble burning
- in areas of gorse, by natural fires
- on heathlands by deliberate burning to regenerate the cover of heath.

Source: Nagle, G., 1997, 'Fire', Geography Review, 11, 2, 22–5

Soil organic matter loss and deteriorating soil structure

Soil organic matter is a vital component of productive and stable soils. It is an important source of plant nutrients, improves water retention and soil structure, and is important in terms of the soil's buffering capacity (filtering out pollutants) against many of the threats listed on page 79.

Over the last fifty years many areas of permanent grassland have been ploughed up and used for arable agriculture. Repeated cultivation, removal of the vegetation (the crop), and a reduction in the use of organic manures has resulted in a rapid reduction of the organic matter content of these soils.

Since 1980 there has been an increase in the proportion of agricultural soils which have organic matter concentrations of less than 3.7%, and a decrease in the percentage of soils with a organic matter of more than 7%. The ploughing of grasslands, the loss of meadows, and arable rotation has lead to a decrease in organic matter in many soils. Low organic contents are related to higher rates of erosion.

CHANGING SOILS

Agricultural soils are altered by frequent ploughing and mixing, which prevent the normal development of soils.

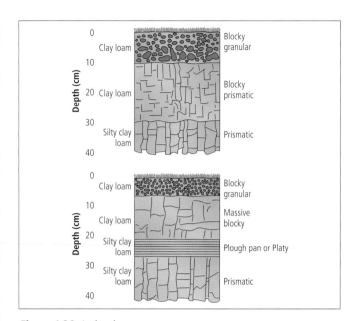

Figure 4.26 *A plough pan*
Source: Nagle, G. and Spencer, K., 1997, Advanced geography revision handbook, OUP

In general, agricultural soils have more plant nutrients than natural soils, but less organic matter. Ploughing affects soil chemistry and biology, structure and texture. In addition, soils that are ploughed when wet and easily moulded may develop a plough pan (Figure 4.26).

The optimum soil for cultivation has a pH of 5.5–7.0. Chemical fertilisers have been used since the nineteenth century, although manuring and marling (adding lime) have been important for centuries. The basic artificial fertilisers are a combination of N, P and K – nitrogen, phosphorus and potassium. Calcium, nitrogen, potassium and phosphorus are stored in the ground for long periods, hence if fertilisers are used over a long period of time the soil chemistry is altered. Soils that are manured for long periods have a high proportion of phosphate, and may even develop a phosphate-rich horizon. Under natural conditions calcium salts

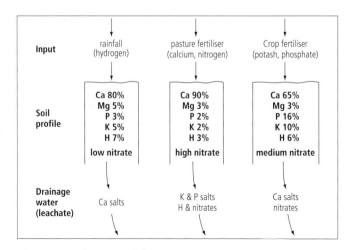

Figure 4.27 *Changing soil chemistry*
Source: Drew. D., 1984, Man-environment processes, George Allen and Unwin

are leached from soils (Figure 4.27(a)). In a pastoral soil, K and P salts are released, while hydrogen and nitrates are leached (Figure 4.27(b)). Under arable conditions (Figure 4.27 (c)) calcium salts and nitrates are leached.

In the last 50 years, inorganic fertiliser applications have increased by between five and ten times to improve agricultural crop yields, and the area of grassland converted to arable use has increased.

The use of heavy machinery may lead to soil compaction. This can have serious consequences for soils. Compaction
- reduces root penetration, especially of young, growing plants
- limits the exchange of gases between the roots and the atmosphere – without air, certain bacteria specialise, which could lead to gleying
- lowers the rate of infiltration of water to the soil.

By contrast, certain human activities may improve soils (Figure 4.28). For example, drainage has many advantages for plants:
- a lower water table provides greater depth for roots
- dry soils warm up earlier in the spring
- ploughing is easier on drier soils
- winter freezing will not affect crops.

However, a drop in the water level may lead to an increase in oxidation and a decline of peat bogs. This has important implications for conservation of biodiversity (Chapter 1 *Britain's changing climate*).

In some areas of naturally infertile soils, such as the west coast of Ireland, people have built small areas of artificial soil by building up a thick layer of organic-rich material over the original soil. These **plaggen** soils are formed of lime-rich sand, seaweed and manure. Up to 10 000 tonnes/hectare are needed to make 65 centimetres of soil! The plaggen soil differs from the original soil in many ways:
- pH is higher: 7.5 compared with 6.0
- carbonate content is 109% compared with 0%
- organic content is 5% compared with 0%
- the sand content is 90% compared with 75%.

Overall there is an increase in soil fertility, sufficient to allow small-scale arable farming to take place.

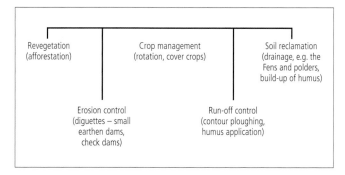

Figure 4.28 *Soil conservation methods*
Source: Nagle, G. and Spencer, K., 1997, Advanced geography revision handbook, OUP

1 **Revegetation**
- deliberate planting
- suppression of fire, grazing etc. to allow regeneration

2 **Measures to stop bank erosion**

3 **Measures to stop gulley enlargement**
- planting of trailing plants etc.
- construction of weirs, dams, gabions etc.

4 **Crop management**
- maintaining a cover at critical times of the year
- rotation
- cover crops

5 **Slope run-off control**
- terracing
- deep tillage and application of humus
- transverse hillside ditches to intercept run-off
- contour ploughing
- preservation of vegetation strips to limit field width

6 **Prevention of erosion from point sources such as roads, feedlots**
- intelligent geomorphic location
- channelling of drainage water to non-susceptible areas
- covering of banks, cuttings, etc. with vegetation

7 **Suppression of wind erosion**
- soil moisture preservation
- increase in surface roughness through ploughing up clods or by planting windbreaks.

Figure 4.29 *Methods of soil conservation*
Source: Goudie, A., 1993, The human impact on the natural environment, Blackwell

QUESTIONS

1 Study Figure 4.28 which shows possible methods of soil conservation.

2 Define the term 'soil conservation'.

3 Explain how any **four** of the methods suggested in Figure 4.29 will lead to increased soil conservation.

4 Which of these methods do you think is best? Justify your choice.

SOIL EROSION

In the UK, widespread attention was first paid to soil erosion in the 1970s. Then soil scientists concentrated on two main problems:
- water erosion of upland peat
- wind erosion on lowland arable fields.

Locally, there were important effects. In the West Midlands, for example, erosion by water was common, leading to gulleying. For example, in a survey of sediment yield in over fifty drainage basins, it was found that over 0.3 tonnes/ha/year was removed. In areas of mixed land use, up to 5 tonnes/ha/year was lost. It is not just the quantity that is important – much of what was eroded was organic-rich top soil.

However, the problem is now regarded as far more wide-spread. About a third of arable land in England and Wales (20 500 square kilometes) has been identified as being at risk from wind or water erosion. The main areas at risk of soil erosion include:

1 lower greensand soils of southern England and the Isle of Wight
2 sandy and loamy soils in Nottinghamshire and the West Midlands
3 sandy and loamy soils in Somerset and Dorset
4 sandy and loamy soils in East Anglia
5 chalk soils of the South Downs, Cambridgeshire, Yorkshire, Lincolnshire Wolds, Hampshire and Wiltshire
6 sandy soils in South Devon
7 loamy soils in eastern Scotland.

In all these places the main agent of erosion is run-off. In addition, wind erosion is important locally on the sandy soils of the Vale of York and the Brecklands of East Anglia, and on the peat mosses of Lancashire. The sandy and loamy soils of the West Midlands and Nottinghamshire are at risk of both wind and water erosion.

The increase in soil erosion is due to a number of factors:

- intensification of agriculture
- heavier and more powerful machinery
- compaction (by increasingly heavy agricultural machinery)
- cultivation of steeper slopes
- field enlargement
- hedgerow removal
- planting of winter cereals.

For example, between 1969 and 1983 there was a three-fold increase in the amount of winter cereals produced in England and Wales, and a fourfold increase in Scotland between 1967 and 1986. The risk of erosion is increased in areas sown with winter cereals until there is at least a 30% crop cover on the field. Moreover, winter drilling (sowing and planting) occurs when the fields are at their wettest, leading to increased run-off and, therefore, loss of seed and soil. In the South Downs, for example, winter cereals occupy 60% of the agricultural area, and run-off travels unimpeded from one large field to another.

Erosion in uplands is due to a combination of water, wind, fire and human activities. In the southern Pennines, gulley-ing has taken place since the start of the Industrial Revolution in the eighteenth century. High pollution levels during the Industrial Revolution killed the protective moss. In addition, there has been a large increase in the number of sheep in the area and this has led to overgrazing.

The impact of soil erosion also includes:

- declining productivity
- decreasing organic and moisture content
- increased turbidity (murkiness) in streams.

Figure 4.30 *An eroded footpath*

Soil erosion can lead to a reduction in soil productivity. Thinner soils hold less water and provide less space for root development. If organic matter is eroded, the water-holding capacity is further reduced. If nutrients are eroded, soil fertility is reduced still further. In addition, erosion by water may lead to soil compaction.

It is not only agriculture that leads to erosion. Recreational impacts are well known for their detrimental effects (Figures 4.30 and 4.31). (See also The environmental impact of recreation, in *Development and underdevelopment* in this series).

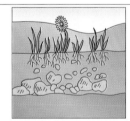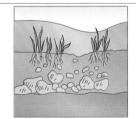

1 Good vegetation cover and level soil surface. Vegetation keeps the soil together and aerates it. Rainfall is able to percolate into the ground.

2 Trampling compacts the soil. The infiltration rate is reduced and overland run-off increases. Trampling reduces the vegetation cover, consequently the soil is neither bound nor aerated.

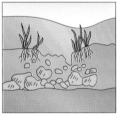

3 Erosion of the surface accelerates. Gullies may be formed and the bedrock is exposed. Very little vegetation survives.

4 The rough, irregular, stony surface is unattractive to walkers and may even be dangerous. As a result, walkers begin to use the vegetated areas at the side of the footpath and the process begins again.

Figure 4.31 *Model of footpath erosion*
Source: Nagle, G. and Spencer, K., 1996, Investigating geography, Hodder and Stoughton

QUESTIONS

1 Study Figure 4.31 which shows a model evolution of footpath erosion in a heavily used area.

2 Using this, explain the effects that frequent trampling across a school sports field, for example, might have.

3 Using the USLE explain the high rates of soil erosion on the South Downs.

The universal soil loss equation (USLE) states that A = RKLSCP where

A   is the annual soil loss
R   is the erosivity (potential for erosion) of the rain
K   is the erodability (susceptibility) of the soil
L   is the length of slope
S   is slope angle
C   is the crop management factor and
P   is soil conservation.

SUMMARY

Soils are an extremely important part of geography. Food production, and therefore a major part of world trade, depend upon a healthy soil. We have seen how on a very small scale soils vary greatly. They therefore make a very good subject for geographical investigations – and the data is literally under our feet. Nevertheless, the many factors that affect soils, and the processes that create them, make soils a complex feature. In addition, we have seen that the human impact on soils has been largely negative, although not entirely so. Increasingly, we are aware that the soil is a non-renewable resource, a precious commodity, in need of sustainable development and management.

QUESTIONS

1 Examine the effects of climate and geology on soil formation.
2 Describe the main processes that affect soils in the British Isles.
3 For a small area that you have studied, describe and explain local variations in soil types and processes.
4 With the use of examples, discuss the effects of human activity on soils.

INVESTIGATIVE WORK

There are many simple but excellent projects that can be carried out on soils. For example we could test:
- how erosion varies across a footpath
- how soil moisture content and organic content are related
- how slope angle affects soil thickness
- how soils vary with geology.

A number of techniques can be used for presenting and analysing the data. For example:
- a scatter graph and a line of best fit show variations in moisture and organic content
- Spearman's rank correlation coefficient tests whether there is a relationship between variables (see *Development and underdevelopment* in this series for worked examples of Spearman's rank correlation coefficient, and scatter graphs)
- triangular graphs show variations in the composition of the soil.

Soils allow us to obtain a great deal of information from a small area of study. Two of the most interesting aspects of soils are the moisture content and the organic content. Measuring these is quite easy.
Take a sample of soil with a soil auger or a small trowel.
Place a handful of soil in an air-tight bag.
To measure moisture content weigh a sample of soil (S1). Place it in an oven and heat it at 100°C for twenty-four hours. Reweigh the dried sample (S2).
To work out the moisture content of the sample use the formula:

$$\text{moisture content} = \frac{S1 - S2}{S1} \times 100\%$$

To measure organic content, take the sample (S2) and burn it over a bunsen burner at maximum heat for fifteen minutes to burn off the organic content. Reweigh the burned sample (S3).
To work out the organic content use the formula:

$$\text{organic content} = \frac{S2 - S3}{S2} \times 100\%$$

BIBLIOGRAPHY AND RECOMMENDED READING

Boardman, J., and Evans, R., 1994, *Soil erosion in Britain: a review*, in **Rickson, R.,** 1994, *Conserving soil resources: European perspectives*, CAB International
Drew, D., 1984, *Man-environment processes*, George Allen and Unwin
Goudie, A., 1993, *The human impact*, 4th edition, Blackwell
HMSO, 1992, *The UK environment*, HMSO
HMSO, 1996, *Indicators of sustainable development for the UK*, HMSO
Knapp, B., 1979, *Soil processes*, George Allen and Unwin
Wild, A., 1996, *Soils and the environment*, Cambridge University Press

WEB SITES

Ministry of Agriculture, Fisheries and Food – http://www.open.gov.uk/maff/maffhome.htm
Environment Agency – http://www.environment-agency.gov.uk/

Chapter 5
Ecosystems

Ecology and ecosystems have become popular terms in recent decades. The rise of the 'Green Movement' and 'green issues' has led to an increased awareness of ecological issues. In this chapter we look at the structure of ecosystems, the way in which they work, and the major ecosystems of the British Isles. A major part of this chapter examines the human impact upon these ecosystems. In particular we examine the nature of urban ecosystems, an increasingly popular part of the study of geography.

THE STRUCTURE OF ECOSYSTEMS

Biogeography is the geographic distribution of soils, vegetation and ecosystems: where they are and why they are there. An **ecosystem** is the interrelationship between plants, animals, their living and non-living environments. Ecosystems vary in scale from a dead tree trunk to global ecosystems (Figure 5.1). Some ecosystems, such as a pond or tree trunk, have distinct boundaries, whereas others, such as deserts, do not.

All ecosystems are open systems because of the flow of energy (sunlight) and matter (organisms, abiotic elements) across their boundary (Figure 5.2).

Ecosystems can be divided into two main components:

- **abiotic** – (non-living) elements, e.g. air, water, heat, nutrients, rock and sediments
- **biotic** – (living) elements, e.g. plants and animals. Biotic elements can be divided into two main groups:
  - **autotrophs** (or producers) are organisms capable of converting sunlit energy into food energy by photosynthesis. These are normally green plants that use energy, water and carbon dioxide to produce carbohydrates (photosynthesis), but it also includes plankton.
  - **heterotrophs** (or consumers) are organisms that must feed on other organisms to survive. These include:
- **herbivores** – plant eaters
- **carnivores** – meat eaters
- **omnivores** – plant and meat eaters
- **detritivores** – decomposers, bacteria and fungi.

Trophic systems

The **trophic** classification or system is based on feeding patterns (Figure 5.3). At its most simple the trophic classification includes three levels:

- autotrophs (green plants and producers) are the first trophic level
- herbivores (plant eaters) are the second trophic level
- carnivores (meat eaters) are the third trophic level.

Figure 5.1 A natural and an agricultural ecosystem

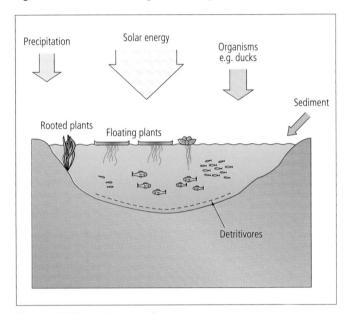

Figure 5.2 The pond as a simple ecosystem
Source: Nagle, G. and Spencer, K., 1997, Advanced geography revision handbook, OUP

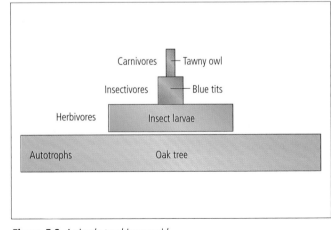

Figure 5.3 A simple trophic pyramid
Source: Nagle, G. and Spencer, K., 1997, Advanced geography revision handbook, OUP

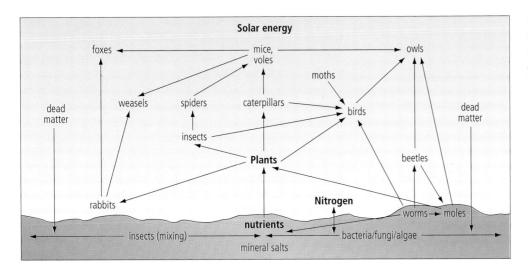

Figure 5.4 *A food web in a deciduous forest*
Source: Nagle, G. and Spencer, K., 1997, Advanced geography revision handbook, OUP

Food chains and food webs

Food chains are simple linear feeding sequences. Food is passed from producer (plant) to herbivore to carnivore. For example, in a deciduous forest, caterpillars feed on the vegetation. In turn, the caterpillars are eaten by birds such as blue tits, which are eaten by tawny owls. In reality some animals, such as foxes, will eat both animals and plants and therefore cannot be put into one category. In addition, there may be many levels of consumers. Hence, complex food webs rather than food chains are found (Figure 5.4). Organisms which feed at the same level on the food chain are said to be at the same **trophic level**.

Energy flow and biomass

Sunlight energy fixed by green plants is passed through the ecosystem by food chains and webs from one trophic level to the next. As energy is passed through the system it is stored at various trophic levels. The storage of energy – the amount of the living matter present – is referred to as **biomass** or **standing crop**. It is measured in terms of dry weight, ash weight, or calorific value per unit area.

The flow of energy decreases with each successive trophic level so less biomass will be supported at the higher trophic levels. Typically there is a trophic pyramid, showing more plant biomass and less consumer biomass. This occurs because:

- no energy transfer is 100% efficient – the transfer of light energy to food energy is only 1% efficient
- there are large losses of energy at each trophic level due to respiration, growth, reproduction and mobility, etc.

Productivity

Productivity refers to the rate of energy production, normally on an annual basis:

- **primary productivity** refers to plant productivity
- **secondary productivity** refers to that produced by animals
- **gross productivity** is the total amount of energy fixed
- **net productivity** is the amount of energy left after losses of respiration, growth, etc. are taken into account
- **net primary productivity (NPP)** is the amount of energy made available by plants to animals at the herbivore level.

Figure 5.5 *Productivity and biomass in global ecosystems*
Source: Simmons, I., 1979, Biogeography: natural and cultural, Arnold

Ecosystem	Mean NPP kg/m^2/yr	Mean biomass kg/m^2	NPP/biomass (column 3)
Tropical rainforest	2.2	45	
Tropical deciduous forest	1.6	35	
Tropical scrub	0.37	3	
Savanna	0.9	4	
Mediterranean sclerophyll	0.5	6	
Desert	0.003	0.002	
Temperate grassland	0.6	1.6	
Temperate forest	1.2	32.5	
Boreal forest	0.8	20	
Tundra and mountain	0.14	0.6	
Open ocean	0.12	0.003	
Continental shelf	0.36	0.001	
Estuaries	1.5	1	

Productivity is often expressed as kg/m²/yr (kilograms per square metre per year). NPP depends upon the amount of heat, moisture, nutrient availability, competition, sunlight hours, age of plants and health of plant. In geographic terms, NPP increases towards the equator, given a sufficient supply of water, and declines towards the poles. Of all light energy reaching the vegetation surface, only between 1–5% is trapped as food energy (enough to maintain life). Moreover, natural systems are more productive than agricultural systems.

Energy flows and productivity are very difficult to assess accurately, as many species have different roles and cannot be placed easily in one trophic layer. For example, very few carnivores only eat meat. Hence energy flows are rarely simple; frequently there is **feedback**: some species eat faeces, so energy in the faecal material does not go to the decomposer (detritivore) but to the system at a lower trophic level.

Gersmehl's nutrient cycles

The flow of energy in an ecosystem is one way – light energy to heat energy, stored and then lost. By contrast, nutrients are circulated and re-used frequently. All natural elements are capable of being absorbed by plants, as gases or soluble salts. Only oxygen, carbon, hydrogen and nitrogen are needed in large quantities. These are known as **macronutrients**. The rest are **trace elements** or **micronutrients**, for example magnesium, sulphur, and phosphorus. These are needed only in small doses.

Nutrients are taken in by plants and built into new organic matter. When animals eat the plants they take up the nutrients, and eventually return them to the soil when they die and the carcass is broken down by the decomposers.

Nutrient cycles consist of a **reservoir pool**, a large, slow moving, inorganic component, and an **exchange pool**, a smaller, more active component where nutrients are exchanged between biotic and abiotic elements. All nutrient cycles involve interaction between the soil and the atmosphere and involve many food chains. Nevertheless, there is great variety between the cycles. Generally, gaseous (atmospheric-based) cycles are more complete than sedimentary ones, as the latter are more susceptible to disturbance, especially by human activity.

Nutrient cycles can be sedimentary-based, i.e. the source of the nutrient is from rocks, or they can be atmospheric based, as in the case of the nitrogen cycle. Nutrient cycles can be shown by means of simplified diagrams – indicating the stores of nutrients as well as the transfers. The most important factors which determine these differences in nutrient cycles are availability of moisture, heat, fire (in grasslands), density of vegetation, competition and length of growing season.

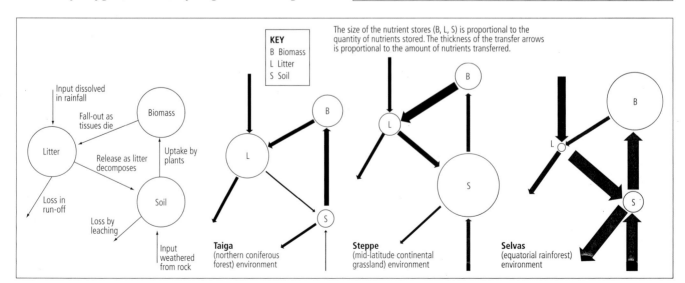

Figure 5.6 *Gersmehl's model of nutrient cycles*
Source: Nagle, G. and Spencer, K., 1997, Advanced geography revision handbook, OUP

Succession

Succession or **prisere**, refers to the sequential changes in a plant community as it moves towards a **seral climax**. Succession is determined by a number of factors:

- the supply of new species
- environmental stress, such as a lack of water or nutrients
- competition between species.

Succession is brought about by a change in the micro-environment by each **sere** which alters the micro-environment and allows another group of species to dominate. The **climax community** is the group of species that are at a **dynamic equilibrium** with the prevailing environmental conditions. Dynamic equilibrium occurs when features, such as vegetation or soil, are in balance with the surrounding environment. As the environment changes, so too does the feature.

In the UK, under natural conditions, the climax community would be oak woodland. On a global scale, climate is the most important factor in determining large scale vegetation groupings, or **biomes**, such as tropical rainforest and temperate grassland. However, in some areas, distribution of vegetation may be influenced more by soils than climate. This is known as **edaphic** control. In savanna areas, forests dominate clay soils and grassland dominates sandy soils. On a local scale, within a climatic region, soils may affect

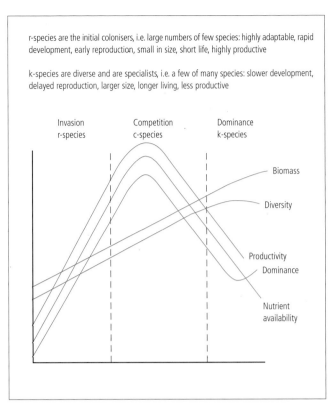

r-species are the initial colonisers, i.e. large numbers of few species: highly adaptable, rapid development, early reproduction, small in size, short life, highly productive

k-species are diverse and are specialists, i.e. a few of many species: slower development, delayed reproduction, larger size, longer living, less productive

Figure 5.7 *Succession and species selection*
Source: Nagle, G. and Spencer, K., 1997, Advanced geography revision handbook, OUP

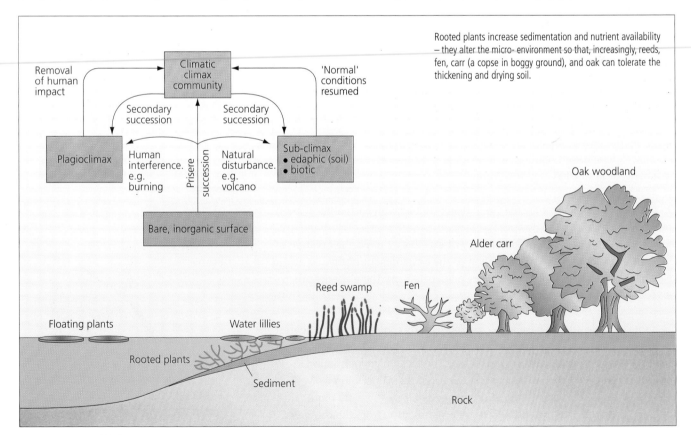

Figure 5.8 *A model of succession*
Source: Nagle, G. and Spencer, K., 1997, Advanced geography revision handbook, OUP

plant groupings; for example, on the Isle of Purbeck grass-land is found on limestone and chalk rendzina soils, forest on the brown earths and heathland on the podzols associated with sands and gravels (see Chapter 4, page 74).

A **plagioclimax** refers to a plant community permanently influenced by people, that is, it is prevented from reaching climatic climax by burning, grazing and so on. For example, on Britain's heathlands deforestation, burning and grazing have replaced the original oak woodland.

Figure 5.9 *A hydrosere (succession of plants in fresh water) at Shotover, Oxford*

QUESTIONS

1 Describe the sequence of succession shown in Figure 5.8.

2 What evidence is there of any succession in Figure 5.9?

Inset 5.1
Island ecology

Islands are very important in biogeography. Their characteristics include:
- a low species diversity compared with continents
- decreasing diversity with distance from a continent
- larger islands contain more species than smaller islands
- islands are very susceptible to migrations, colonisations and extinctions
- human impact on island ecosystems is potentially great due to their fragile nature.

Because islands are often quite small and have a limited selection of species, human interference can potentially ruin their ecosystems, with limited likelihood of replacement with others of the same species.

Although the world's islands are very diverse in their characteristics, they share a number of important features. In ecological terms, islands can be as large as continents or as small as individual rocks.

On a large scale, when continents are in direct contact with each other there is free movement of species. However, as they drift apart, contact is lost and separate evolutionary patterns occur. A good example of this is the isolation of the Australian continent, which has allowed the development of the marsupials such as the kangaroo, wallaby and koala bear. These species are not found on any other continents.

On a smaller scale, islands have a low species diversity compared to the nearest continental mass – a contributory factor in the instability of islands. For example, Britain has only about a third of the species of mammals found in continental western Europe, and has lost several of them, including wolves, boars, bears and beavers since the Middle Ages; similarly, there are more species in Britain than in Ireland. Diversity decreases away from the continent, as oceans limit the dispersal of flora and fauna.

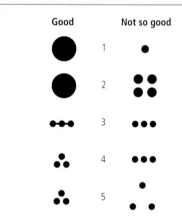

The diagrams show a set of general rules for the design of nature reserves, based on theories of island biogeography.

1   A large reserve will hold larger populations with lower probabilities of going extinct than will a small reserve

2   A single reserve is preferable to a series of smaller reserves of equal total area, since these will support only small populations with relatively high probabilities of going extinct

3-5 If reserves must be fragmented, then they should be connected by corridors of similar vegetation (3) or be placed equidistant (4) and as near to each other as possible (5). In this way immigration rates between the fragments will be increased, thereby maximizing the chances of extinct populations being replaced from elsewhere in the reserve complex

Figure 5.10 *The principles of island biogeography*
Source: Goudie, A., (after Gorman, 1979) 1993, The human impact on the natural environment, Blackwell

The size of an island is an important factor in determining its biogeography (Figure 5.10). The greater the size of the island, the larger the number of species that can be supported. Britain and Ireland illustrate this very well. The relationship between area and species number on an island can be extended to other ecological 'islands' such as lakes, desert oases and sphagnum bogs. If too many species migrate to an island, competition will lead to some species becoming extinct. Hence natural ecosystems (with non-human intervention) are self-regulating. In addition, the diversity of species also depends on other factors, such as the ease of colonisation (colonisation of more distant islands is more difficult) and size of island (range of potential environments).

On a small scale, islands are naturally unstable ecosystems and liable to be upset by human activities. Islands are very susceptible to the effects of migrations, colonisations and extinctions. The lack of means of escape from any natural disasters, such as earthquakes and volcanic eruptions, means that islands are often at a low stage of seral development. Very often there are no top carnivores. In Ireland the top carnivore is the fox, whereas in mainland Europe bears and lynxes are the top carnivores.

The human impact on island ecosystems is potentially great due to their fragility. The direct impact is evident in the clearing of vegetation and killing of whole species, for example the dodo, and the indirect impact is equally important. Indirect impacts include the introduction of alien species, such as rabbits and pheasants in the UK by the Normans and spartina (cord grass) in the 1880s, originally in Southampton, but now dominating many salt marshes along the south coast of England.

Species are often **endemic** (native) to only one or a few islands, and the extinction of species happens easily. The most notable example is the dodo, a flightless bird native to Mauritius which became extinct at the end of the seventeenth century. Very often, new species introduced by man are better competitors than indigenous species and squeeze them out of their ecological niches. In the past, sailors deliberately introduced sheep, goats and pigs to many islands and unintentionally introduced rats. The rats found the flightless birds of many islands (previously with no natural predators) easy prey and they became extinct very quickly.

Why Ireland has fewer species than Britain

Compared with Britain, Ireland has half the number of land mammals (28 out of 55), and less than half the species of resident butterflies (29 out of 60). It has fewer breeding birds (167 out of 229), only four amphibians and reptiles (or five, including the recently introduced slow worm) out of twelve

species native to Britain, and a more limited flora (about 940 flowering plants as opposed to around 1400).

There are several reasons for Ireland's short-fall in species. They are all connected to its status as an island. Firstly, Ireland is much smaller than Britain, covering 83 042 square kilometres, compared to Britain with 230 607 square kilometres. A smaller area means a smaller gene pool, so species that are rare in north-west Europe are less likely to survive. Golden eagles, for example, have become extinct in Ireland, as their overall numbers have dropped, although a few are still found in the Scottish Highlands, a few in the Lake District, and they remain widespread in mainland Europe.

Ireland has also less variety of habitats than the UK and mainland Europe. Its mountain ranges, for example, are neither as high nor as extensive. Consequently alpine birds such as the ptarmigan are absent from Ireland.

Ireland's mild but wet oceanic climate has also inhibited the advance of some species. The pollen record shows that as the ground warmed up after the Ice Age 10 000 years ago, trees spread back across Ireland in orderly succession. First came juniper, followed by willow and birch. After 750 years, around 9250 years ago, hazel and pine took over. These were replaced as climax trees between 8000 and 7000 years ago by oak and elm. As the temperature rose, alder appeared. But the most dramatic change occurred in Europe 5500 years ago when elm almost vanished, accompanied by a sudden rise in weeds associated with cultivation, such as docks, nettles and plantains.

Because the climate of Ireland is mild and wet, and the land has been used for agriculture for nearly 6000 years, Ireland contains few tundra species, which need colder conditions, nor does it have species which need much milder, drier conditions. 6000 years of human activity have influenced strongly the type of vegetation present.

Small area, the limited variety of habitats, climate and history, have also played their part in limiting the number of species that Ireland can support today. The impact of these factors, however, has been increased most of all by relative isolation. Isolation has had its profoundest effect on Ireland's quota of land mammals, reptiles and amphibians which cannot travel by air.

Most of Ireland's contemporary mammals are not, in fact, native to the island. Humans have a hand in the introduction of at least 12 of the 21 land mammals. Some, including the grey squirrel, were brought over deliberately, whereas other common rodents came as stowaways. The only true Irish mammals are the fox, badger, stoat, pine marten, otter, Irish hare, red deer, pygmy shrew and wood mouse (Figure 5.11). The species that made it to Ireland would have been the hardier animals that first began the trek north, after the retreat of the ice sheets 10 000 years ago, from mainland Europe (still joined at that stage). This may explain why Ireland has so few species of reptiles and amphibians. Many British species, like the common toad, the viper, the grass snake and the crested newt, are not found in Ireland.

QUESTIONS

1 What is meant by the term 'island biogeography'?
2 How do islands differ from continental land masses in their ecological characteristics?
3 Why are there no snakes in Ireland?

Figure 5.11 *Native Irish deer in Killarney, Ireland*

Skills:
Planning an essay

When describing and explaining an ecosystem in an essay, you need to think about:

1 a case study or example
2 climate
3 soils
4 vegetation and adaptations
5 nutrient cycles
6 animals and adaptations
7 local conditions, such as relief
8 human impact.

1 A named case study is important. This should give details about location and size of the area. A location map – either global or local – is very useful.

2 Climate details are often best given on a climograph. This is very useful when you are comparing ecosystems and is an easy way of learning and revising details. A written explanation should include:
   (i) precipitation
   • type of precipitation, e.g. rain, snow, dew
   • type of rainfall, e.g. convectional, cyclonic or orographic
   • total precipitation in millimetres
   • seasonality of precipitation, e.g. year round, summer, winter, regular or irregular
   • intensity
   • humidity levels, i.e. dry or damp.

(ii) temperature
   • winter average
   • summer average (these two give the seasonal range)
   • diurnal (daily) range
   • number of days above 0°C (growing season)
   • number of days above 6°C (necessary for tree growth).

(iii) wind
   • global and/or local winds will effect evapotranspiration rates.

3 Soils are best illustrated with a simple diagram. In addition you should write about the following:
   • type of soil: general (pedocal/pedalfer) and specific (brown earth, podzol, rendzina, gley, etc.)
   • horizons
   • main process affecting soil, such as leaching, eluviation, calcification, gleying.

4 Vegetation can be described in a number of ways. It is important to cover the following points:
   • NPP (net primary productivity)
   • biomass.
   • type of vegetation, e.g. (i) trees, grasses, shrubs (ii) dominant species (iii) variety (iv) height (v) diversity (vi) layering and (vii) adaptations.

5 Nutrient cycles link many components of the ecosystem. These should be shown with the use of a diagram and an explanation of the relative sizes of stores and transfers.

6 Animal life should be mentioned, especially if there are significant adaptations to environmental conditions. In most cases it is worth mentioning:
- dominant species and top carnivores in the system
- complexity of food chains and food webs.

7 Many ecosystems are influenced by local conditions. These include:
  - relief
  - aspect
- geology
- altitude.

8 Finally, the human impact on the ecosystem should be discussed. Depending on the question, this may be even more important. Some ecosystems are more affected by human activity than others, and discussion of these should not be left until the end. Even when looking at 'natural' ecosystems you should describe, explain and evaluate the impact of human activity. This human activity needs a case study (with figures) of, for example, agricultural development, urbanisation, industrialisation, deforestation, water development, or tourism.

ECOSYSTEMS IN THE BRITISH ISLES

There are a number of major types of ecosystem in the British Isles (Figure 5.12, see page 92). These include deciduous forests, coniferous forests, heaths, moorlands and wetlands.

Temperate deciduous forest

Vegetation

Deciduous woodlands are dominated by trees 20-30 metres tall. The main species include oak, lime, elm, beech, chestnuts, and maples. Dominance by one or two species is common. The characteristics of these forests are:
- deciduous trees shed their leaves in winter to retain moisture, conserve nutrients and avoid damage by snow/ice
- NPP is high – 1.2 kg/m²/year due to high summer temperatures and the long hours of daylight
- biomass is high – 35kg/m² due to large amounts of woody material.

Vegetation varies with soil type. On more acidic soils, birch and rowan are found, whereas on more alkaline soils, box and maple are found. Oak is a generalist and can tolerate a range of soil conditions (pH5–7.5) and can be found on either. Elm and lime are commonly found on clay soils. On gleyed or wet soils, willow and alder dominate.

The amount of light penetrating the tree canopy determines the amount of vegetation that grows beneath the canopy (Figure 5.12). For example, **heliophytes**, such as the wood anemone, need light and therefore flower early in the year before the trees come into leaf; **sciophytes**, such as dog's mercury and ivy, tolerate darker conditions; sycamore trees have large leaves, allowing very little light to pass through to the ground so little shrub or ground vegetation grows; oak and ash, which have small leaves, allow a great deal of light to pass through and consequently there is rich ground and shrub vegetation.

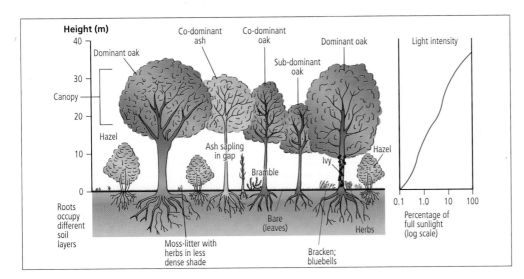

Figure 5.12 *Woodland stratification in a temperate deciduous forest*
Source: O'Hare, G., 1987, Soils, vegetation and ecosystems, Oliver and Boyd

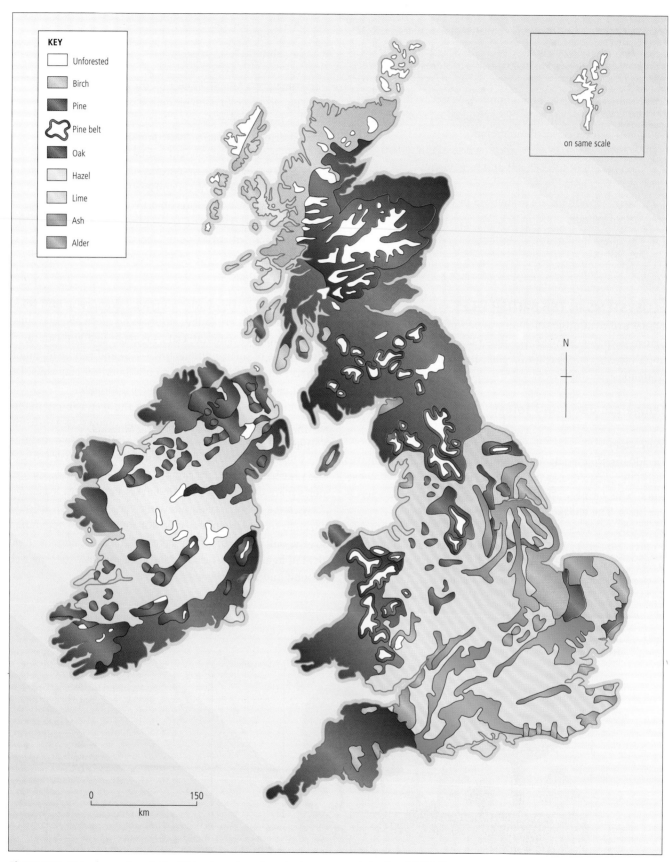

KEY

- Unforested
- Birch
- Pine
- Pine belt
- Oak
- Hazel
- Lime
- Ash
- Alder

on same scale

N

0   150

km

Figure 5.12 *Natural ecosystems in the UK (as shown by major natural ecosystems dating from 3000 BC)*

Source: Goudie, A. and Brunsden, D., 1994, The environment of the British Isles, an atlas, OUP

Climate

The climate associated with deciduous forests is typically mild and wet.

- Rainfall is 500 – 1500 millimetres per year, with a winter maximum (Figure 5.14). It is mostly frontal (cyclonic) rainfall.
- Precipitation is greater than evapotranspiration, e.g. in western Ireland precipitation is 1000 millimetres per year and evapotranspiration is 450 millimetres per year.
- Winter temperatures are above freezing in winter, owing to the North Atlantic Drift.
- Summers are cool, 15–20°C.

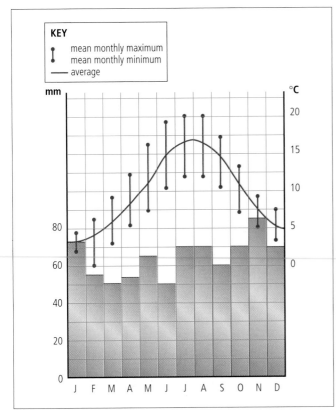

Figure 5.14 *A climatic graph for a deciduous woodland ecosystem (Birmingham)*

Soils

- Soils are generally quite fertile and are brown earths.
- The **mull** humus is mildly acidic (pH 5.5-6.5).
- The litter layer contains a diverse flora and fauna. Soil fauna such as earthworms flourish, mixing the layers and all the nutrients.
- Primary decomposition of vegetation takes place by earthworms, beetles, millipedes and woodlice. Secondary decomposition by mites, including springtails, is followed by bacterial and fungal activity.
- Decomposition of leaves takes up to nine months.
- There are indistinct, blurred horizons, due to mixing by earthworms.

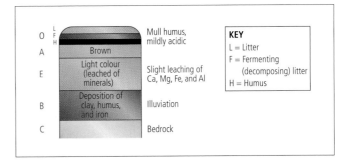

Figure 5.15 *Soil: brown earth*
Source: Nagle, G. and Spencer, K., 1997, Advanced geography revision handbook, OUP

Nutrient cycle

In a deciduous woodland, rates of leaching can be quite high, although this is balanced by relatively fast rates of weathering (Figure 5.16). There is a large store of nutrients in the soil due to:

- slow growth in winter
- a low density of vegetation, compared with tropical rainforest
- an uptake of nutrients about 25% as efficient as the tropical rainforest.

Animals

In the winter months there is a lack of food, leading to a number of adaptations amongst the animals:

- many migrate
- some, like hedgehogs, hibernate
- others, such as squirrels, store food for the winter
- stoats and weasels may change colour (pigmentation), which helps them to catch their prey.

Human impact

The effect of human activity on forest ecosystems has been enormous:

- most areas have been cleared and used for agriculture (since the Second World War, the input of leaf fall has been replaced by chemical and organic fertilisers)
- some forests are heavily managed for recreation, conservation, economic exploitation and research (Figure 5.17, see page 94)
- only a very few areas of natural forest remain.

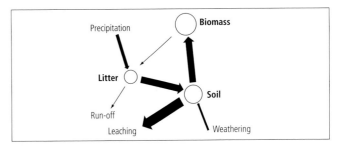

Figure 5.16 *Nutrient cycling in a deciduous woodland*
Source: Nagle, G. and Spencer, K., 1997, Advanced geography revision handbook, OUP

QUESTIONS

1 List **four** species of tree associated with a temperate deciduous forest.

2 Study Figure 5.14. Describe the climate associated with a temperate deciduous forest.

3 Describe the impact of human activity on deciduous woodlands.

Figure 5.17 A managed deciduous woodland

Temperate coniferous (boreal) forest

Vegetation

Coniferous forests are dominated by trees 20-30 metres high. The main species include pine, spruce and larch, but coniferous woodlands are normally dominated by large numbers of a single species.

The characteristics of these forests are:

- limited ground vegetation because it is too dark
- low NPP – 0.8 kg/m²/yr
- a high biomass – 20 kg/m² (much woody matter).

The trees show a number of important adaptations to the environment (Figure 5.18). These include:

- being **evergreen** (green throughout the year) and therefore able to photosynthesise at any time when temperatures rise above 3°C
- having a conical **shape** enabling them to shed snow and reduce rocking by the wind
- having **needle leaves** with a small surface area and reduced water loss
- generally occurring in stands of one species (Figure 5.22), with pine favouring sandy soils and spruce damper soils.

Climate

The climate is a cool temperate or cold continental climate, depending on the proximity of the ocean.

- Rainfall is low, <500 millimetres per year, with no real seasonal pattern (Figure 5.19).

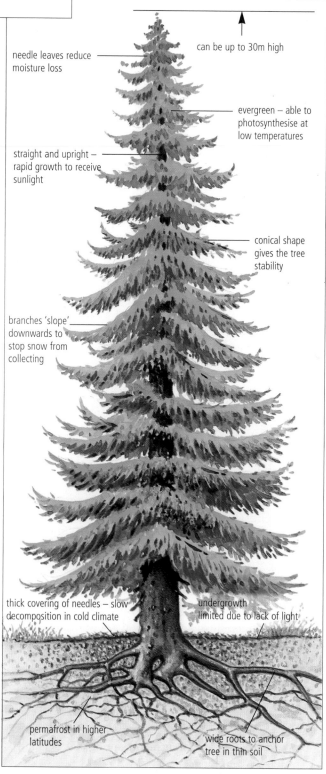

needle leaves reduce moisture loss

can be up to 30m high

evergreen – able to photosynthesise at low temperatures

straight and upright – rapid growth to receive sunlight

conical shape gives the tree stability

branches 'slope' downwards to stop snow from collecting

thick covering of needles – slow decomposition in cold climate

undergrowth limited due to lack of light

permafrost in higher latitudes

wide roots to anchor tree in thin soil

Figure 5.18 Adaptations of conifer trees

Source: Adapted from Money, D., 1978, Climate, soils and vegetation, University Tutorial Press

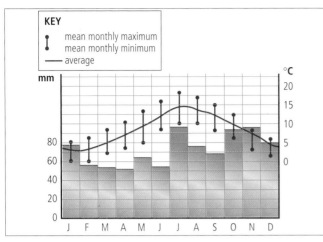

Figure 5.19 *A climatic graph for a coniferous forest*

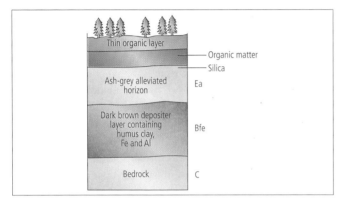

Figure 5.20 *A typical podzol*
Source: Nagle, G. and Spencer, K., 1997, Advanced geography revision handbook, OUP

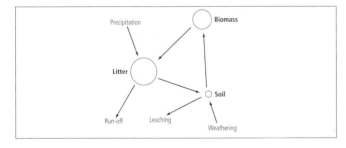

Figure 5.21 *Nutrient cycling in a coniferous woodland*
Source: Nagle, G. and Spencer, K., 1997, Advanced geography revision handbook, OUP

- Precipitation is greater than potential evapotranspiration.
- Snowfall is frequent in winter and frosts occur in summer.
- Summer temperatures reach a maximum of 10–15°C, while winter temperatures can drop below freezing for short periods of time.
- The growing season is limited to 6–8 months, but the long hours of daylight in summer (16–20 hours) allow long hours of photosynthesis.

Soils

The soil typically associated with a coniferous forest is a podzol (Figure 5.20). It has a number of characteristics, which include:

- leaching occurs due to snowmelt rather than rainfall
- there is a raw, acid mor humus with a pH of 4.5–5.5
- the acid water releases iron and aluminium oxides, and moves them down the soil. These oxides may form an impermeable iron pan
- there are very few earthworms, due to the acidity of the soil, hence there is little mixing of the horizons
- thick litter layer develops, due to the low temperatures, and acidic nature of the needle leaves, resistant to decomposition.

Nutrient cycle

Low temperatures and slow rates of weathering produce large stores of nutrients in the litter layer (Figure 5.21).

Animals

The animal population in a coniferous forest is quite sparse. This is because of the poor quality forage, the lack of variety of food types and the lack of light reaching the forest floor. Hence the bird and animal species are fewer. Mammals include voles and occasionally deer in winter. Typical birds include crows, owls, crossbills, pigeons and wrens.

Human impact

Human impact has been significant. Unlike deciduous woodlands (which have been cut down) many coniferous woodlands have been planted (Figure 5.22). This is because they are faster growing, and forestry companies can get a return on their investment after 15–20 years, compared with 50–60 years for deciduous forests.

Figure 5.22 *Coniferous woodland*

QUESTIONS

1 How does the number of species in a coniferous woodland compare with a deciduous woodland?

2 Why are the soils associated with coniferous woodlands usually leached soils?

3 Compare and contrast the nutrient cycle of a coniferous woodland with that of a deciduous woodland.

CHANGES IN WOODLAND HABITATS

Over much of the UK, the natural climax vegetation (the plant communities which would develop and be present in the absence of human intervention) is forest dominated by oak, ash and lime. However, most of the UK's natural forest has been replaced (Figure 5.23).

Today, forests and woodlands make up about 10% of the UK's surface area. Much of this woodland has been established relatively recently on sites which have not been wooded for a long time. Only 15% of the woodland area is ancient in origin, i.e. present since pre-1600. These surviving ancient semi-natural woodlands, many of which have been managed in the past, are, particularly in England, small isolated areas surrounded by intensively farmed land, and are greatly changed in their plants and animals from the ancestral forest. The changes have been brought about by many generations of human management, with selective felling, coppicing and in some cases replanting, changing the proportions of tree and shrub species.

In addition, government policies have had an effect on the forests, in particular the tax policies of the late 1980s which allowed wealthy individuals to replace natural vegetation with coniferous plantations. More recently, in the mid-1990s, Community Forests have been planned and some saplings planted. The largest Community Forest is the 500 square kilometre National Forest across parts of Staffordshire, Derbyshire and Leicestershire. It should reach maturity by 2015.

Coppicing

One of the most common features of forest management has been coppicing. Coppicing means cutting down trees to near ground level every few years (Figure 5.24) to encourage evenly-sized shoots which are more useful economically. The wood is often used to make fencing.

Coppiced woodlands are very different in appearance from natural forests. They have an open, sunny feel with relatively few mature trees to avoid shading out the coppice regrowth. In these forests there are broad tracks, used to extract the timber and wood during winter. The tradition of managing woodlands as coppices has favoured some wildlife at the expense of others. Early succession species (Figure 5.7, see page 87) have an advantage over species associated with ancient trees and dead wood. However, increased planting of non-native tree species is replacing coppiced woodland in many remaining woodland sites. This has resulted in the decline of plants associated with the early successional stages of coppice.

A practice related to coppicing, but practised on a smaller scale, is **pollarding**. Pollarding involves cutting trees down to a height of about two metres. This is above the level which browsing animals, such as deer and goats, can reach on their hind feet.

Figure 5.23 *The decline of Britain's forests*
Source: Swan, The Telegraph Magazine, 10 March 1990

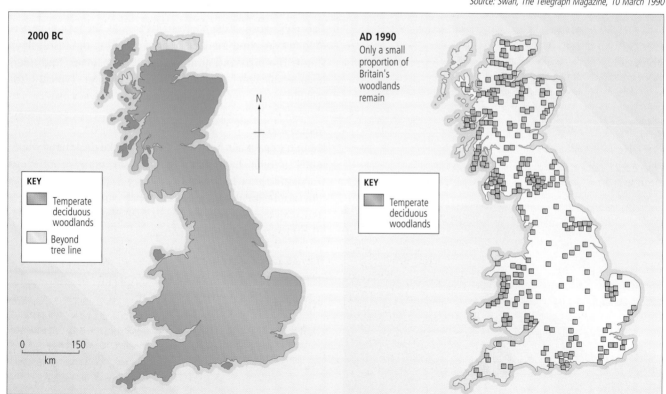

Figure 5.24 Coppicing near Port Meadow, Oxford

Impact of farming

In the late 1980s, a survey of ash trees in Britain showed that almost 20% of all these trees were dying back. This was caused by the way in which the land was managed. Particularly high levels of damage were evident in trees close to arable land. Uncontrolled stubble burning, the effects of drifting herbicides and the consequences of excessive nitrate fertilisers were seen as possible causes. In addition, root disturbance and soil compaction by large agricultural machinery was also to blame. Ash trees in particular have shallow roots and if these are damaged repeatedly, the tree's uptake of water and nutrients may be seriously reduced, while broken root surfaces will become prone to infection by fungi.

It is not just trees in forests that have been affected. The loss of hedgerows has reduced the amount of tree cover. Between 1984 and 1990, there was a net loss of 23% of hedges (about 130 000 kilometres) in Britain. The loss of hedges was the result of a combination of hedge removal and hedge degradation, and it occurred despite the planting/regeneration of about 50 000 kilometres of hedges. In addition, the quality of hedgerows has decreased; between 1978 and 1990, on average one plant species was lost from each ten metres of hedge, an 8% loss of plant species diversity.

Tree or shrub	No. of insect species
Oak	284
Willow	266
Birch	229
Hawthorn	149
Blackthorn	109
Poplar	97
Crab apple	93
Scots pine	91
Alder	90
Elm	82
Hazel	73
Beech	64
Ash	41
Spruce	37*
Lime	31
Hornbeam	28
Rowan	28
Maple	26
Juniper	20
Larch	17*
Fir	16*
Sycamore	15*
Holly	7
Sweet chestnut	5*
Horse chestnut	4*
Yew	4
Walnut	4*
Holme oak	2*
Plane	1*

* introduced species

Figure 5.25 Insect species associated with common trees and shrubs in Britain
Source: HMSO, 1994, Biodiversity, HMSO

HEATHLANDS

Heathlands are developed on soil which is lacking in nutrients. Some heathlands are natural, such as those associated with lowland sands and gravels, glacial outwash, and sands in coastal areas. Others are the result of human activity over long periods of time. These activities include:

- deforestation
- overgrazing
- the use of fire.

Hence, some heathland ecosystems are a plagioclimax, that is their formation depends upon human activity.

Heathland is also limited in its distribution by soil and climatic factors. It occurs where rainfall is 600-1000 millimetres per year, evenly distributed over the year. Even within this climatic and soil regime, however, heathland is fragmented, and disappearing rapidly. Many are threatened by:

- dense scrub and bracken encroaching on them
- too little grazing and cutting
- uncontrolled fire
- housing and industrial developments (Figure 5.26, see page 98).

QUESTIONS

1 How do introduced species differ from native species in terms of numbers of insect species supported?

2 What are the implications of this for food chains and biodiversity?

3 How do coniferous species and deciduous species differ in terms of the number of insect species they support?

Figure 5.26 Heathlands

Year	Hectares (000s)
1750	39.6
1811	30.4
1896	22.67
1934	18.22
1960	10.0
1978	5.83
1992	5.6

Figure 5.27 *The decline of Dorset's heathlands*

Britain has three main types of heath:

- lowland heath – found mainly in southern England: in Breckland (on the border between Norfolk and Suffolk); the Suffolk Sandling (on the Suffolk coast); the Ashdown Forest in Kent; Surrey; Hampshire (mainly in the New Forest); Dorset and Devon
- upland heath – heather moorland, found mainly in the north and west of Britain
- maritime heath found on exposed coasts mainly in Scotland, Wales and south-west England.

Lowland heaths

Heathlands are dominated by heather vegetation, which is normally less than 1 metre high. The vegetation is evergreen, and can tolerate the low nutrient status of the soil. Common species include cotton grass, heather (erica), ling (calluna), bilberry, gorse and broom.

Lowland heaths occur mainly in western Europe. In the late 1990s, Britain had 5600 hectares left, 40% of the world total. Over the past 200 years much of Britain's lowland heath has disappeared:

- 85% of Breckland's heaths
- 75% of Surrey's heaths
- 3% of Hampshire's heaths
- 80% of Dorset's heaths (Figure 5.27).

The loss and fragmentation of Dorset heathlands has been well documented. In the mid-eighteenth century there were about 39 960 hectares of heaths in Dorset; by 1983 5670 hectares remained. The remaining patches of heath are separated from each other by farmland, plantations or buildings, each of which are inhospitable terrain for most heathland species to cross. Since 1983, more than 400 of the remaining 5000 Dorset hectares have been destroyed. Most has been ploughed up to grow cereals, conifers or used for houses and factories.

Over the past 60 years, 80% of the Suffolk Sandling heathland has been destroyed. Today less than 1500 hectares, fragmented into 42 separate sites, survives. In just 100 years, between 1880 and the early 1980s, a third of the heathland area was ploughed up. A third was destroyed between the two world wars, but much of the rest of the destruction has been since the 1950s, to make way for intensive agriculture and afforestation programmes. In addition, housing developments, sand and gravel extraction, golf courses, and industrial developments have destroyed a further 15%; the RAF have developed 5%.

Much of what remains is threatened by other more competitive species such as bracken, birch and pine. This is due to three main factors:

- many heathlands are no longer used for sheep grazing
- rabbit populations have declined due to the introduction of the myxamatosis disease
- the use of fire has been regulated, to reduce the hazards.

Hence many of the processes which favoured heather over other species have disappeared.

QUESTION

1 Study Figure 5.27.

a) Choose a suitable method to show the decline of Dorset's heathlands since 1750, as shown in Figure 5.27.

b) Describe the results you have shown, i.e. when was the decline most rapid?

Moorlands

Upland heaths or moorlands are associated with thin acidic soils, such as those produced by the breakdown of granite, and with high levels of rainfall. They are characterised by:

- sphagnum (bog moss) and purple moor grass on drier areas
- blanket bog, consisting of bog moss, cotton grass, and rushes in very wet areas
- poor drainage
- damp peaty soils
- highland areas, generally above 250 metres, such as parts of the Lake District, Peak District and North York Moors
- lowland areas which are poorly drained and have damp, acidic soils, such as those found on the Somerset Levels.

	Heathland	Moorland
Vegetation Soil Geology	• heather (erica/ericoid/calluna) • podzol • outwash sands and gravels, coastal sands	• sphagnum (moss) • gleyed soil, peaty soils • uplands: hard igneous rock/metamorphic, granite, basalt; lowland clay
Rainfall Altitude Human impact	• 800 mm • low, below 250 m • urbanisation, mineral extraction, recreation	• highland areas >2000 mm; lowlands 800–1000 • high, above 300 m except clay, e.g. Otmoor, Oxfordshire • not very good for agriculture or urbanisation but increasingly used for afforestation, recreation (grouse moors)
Adaptations of plants	• fire-regeneration (burning heather increases productivity)	• sphagnum extracts nutrients directly from atmosphere

Figure 5.28 A comparison of lowland heathlands and moorlands

The soils associated with moorlands are sometimes referred to as organic or peaty soils. True peat has an organic layer more than 38 centimetres deep, whereas peaty soils have an organic layer less than 38 centimetres deep. Wet conditions associated with moorlands include high precipitation, frequent flooding and high water tables. These favour the accumulation of organic matter, which could lead to the formation of peat.

In upland areas, blanket bogs and raised bogs occur above the water table. They are formed from the remains of plants which accumulate to become peat. The absence of oxygen, because of waterlogging, prevents organisms such as bacteria and fungi from breaking down dead organic matter (DOM), and recycling the nutrients. The accumulation of peat over time raises the land surface so that eventually a domed bog surface is created (a raised bog). The only water which reaches the peat surface under these conditions comes from rainfall, so that the nutrients available from ground water are absent; bog plants adapt to cope with this.

Upland peat is associated with sphagnum which grows vigorously when nourished only by rain water and very small amounts of nutrients. It has a great capacity for capturing and storing water. As rainfall increases, sphagnum thrives and builds up into small mounds or hummocks.

Lowland peat depends on high ground water tables. Typical lowland vegetation includes reed swamp, and carr.

Figure 5.29 Moorlands

WETLAND HABITATS

Wetlands cover about 6% of the earth's surface, mainly in small patches, but they account for about 25% of the earth's net primary productivity (annual growth of leaves). They have a diverse range of organisms and provide crucial wintering, breeding and refuge areas for wildlife.

Fresh water habitats are conventionally separated into standing water (lakes, ponds and pools) and running water (rivers, streams and springs). Britain has a large number of lakes and ponds: over 4500 water bodies which are larger than four hectares have been recorded and although estimates vary, there are probably over 300 000 ponds of under one hectare.

Wetlands can be divided into bogs, which are fed only by rainfall, and fens (mineral marshes) which are fed by streams, rivers and springs or seepages as well as rainfall. Plants derive their nutrients from the soil and water in the soil, hence these soils are more fertile than moorlands. Both fens and bogs are rich in biological diversity, with plants such as reeds, alder, sallow and willow, which are adapted to wet conditions and can tolerate waterlogged terrain.

Bogs

Bogs are waterlogged areas with a surface layer of decaying vegetation. They are characterised by sphagnum moss and cotton grass. Bogs are common in Dartmoor, the Pennines and the west coast of Scotland.

Fens

Fens are widely distributed in the UK with more small sites in comparison to bogs. The larger fens, such as those in East Anglia, have a long history of drainage or agriculture. In the 1990s, in East Anglia, an area of about 25 000 hectares has been reduced to four small sites of less than 500 hectares each, with the loss of many fenland species, such as the large copper butterfly. Unlike bogs, many fens have long established management schemes, such as the cutting of reeds and sedges for thatching. This maintains plant communities such as common reed and saw sedge. Fens contain a diverse

Figure 5.30 *Agricultural ecosystem*

array of water tolerant plants such as reeds, sedges, milk parsley, bog myrtle and grass of Parnassus, and trees such as alder and birch.

AGRICULTURAL ECOSYSTEMS

Agricultural ecosystems can be measured in terms of productivity, biomass, nutrient cycling and energy efficiency. Average productivity from agricultural systems is 0.65 kg/m^2/year, comparable with temperate grasslands or prairies. However, only about 0.25% of incoming radiation is utilised by crops, and of that less than 1% is used by people as food. Harvesting removes a large proportion of nutrients from agricultural ecosystems (Figure 5.30).

Human activities have altered the original distribution patterns and habitat associations of wildlife in British landscapes. The rates of change in the environment brought about by humans, for example by pollution and land-use changes, far exceed those at which species can adapt. This has two major effects:

- the rate of loss of species far exceeds the development of new species and thus the global genetic pool is diminished (and can never be replaced)
- the habitats within which the remaining species reside are irredeemably diminished.

Flora and fauna

An article in *Nature* in March 1914 stated:

'It is only too true that man is slowly but surely destroying the beautiful wild animals and plants of the world and is substituting for them queer domesticated races which suit his convenience and his greed, or else is blasting whole territories with the dirt and deadly refuse of his industries and converting well watered forest lands into lifeless deserts by the ravages of the axe.'

The article continued:

'The "country" with its manured fields, its well trimmed hedges and artificial barriers, its parks planted with foreign trees and shrubs, its roadways stinking of tar and petrol and its streams converted into chemical drains or else into overstocked fish stews, is only rendered less repulsive than the town by the survival here and there of a pond or a copse or a bit of ancient moorland (happily too swampy for golfers) where nature is still allowed to pursue her own way.'

The clearance of about 90% of the UK's forests in the past 5000 years has been detrimental to many species dependent upon forest conditions. Much of the land surface is now farmed, forested or worked upon, even the most remote hills and mountains, such as the Shetlands and Hebrides, are grazed or trampled. Forest clearance began in Neolithic times (some 10 000 years ago). From Roman times, the British landscape became clearly dominated by human activities, with succeeding cultures having greater and greater impact. By the Middle Ages many woodland boundaries were similar to those of today and cultivation and grazing by livestock accounted for much of the remaining land.

In the late eighteenth century, the Enclosure Acts changed patterns of land ownership and subsistence farming was replaced by the production of crops for sale on the open market, rather than domestic or local consumption. At the time of the Industrial Revolution the increasing urban population made new demands on land for housing, industry and transport. Woodland management and new plantations reflected growing demands for timber, although the demands were mostly satisfied by imports from forests in North America and elsewhere.

A further consequence of industrial growth was the increasing pollution of air and water, leading to a dramatic reduction in ranges of lichens and fresh water species in rivers. Throughout the nineteenth century, land drainage and more sophisticated farming practices increased agricultural production, but at the expense of many wetlands and ancient grasslands, together with their characteristic wildlife. For unimproved lowland grasslands in the UK, it is estimated that over 97% were lost between 1932 and 1984. For lowland heathlands in England, over 70% were lost between 1830 and 1980.

Similarly, changes in agricultural activity in recent decades have accelerated the loss of many landscapes and animal populations. Restoration of biodiversity is time consuming and expensive. What is easy to lose quickly is hard to regain, even slowly. Many bird species typical of lowland farming in the UK have undergone pronounced decline since the mid-1970s. These include the well-documented declines of the grey partridge, barn owl and lapwing. A large number of other, more common farmland bird species have also severely declined over the last two decades. For example, ten out of twelve seed-eating birds found on farmlands showed signs of decline in numbers between 1977 and 1991, including:

Forestry practices	Water	Soil	Landscapes	Nature and wildlife
Wood production:				
Planting	• Accumulation of litter from acidifying tree species → soil acidification → groundwater acidification • Cultivation of productive water-demanding tree species reducing groundwater availability	• Accumulation of litter from acidifying tree species → soil acidification	• Uniform planting → major changes in form, colour and texture arising from sharp boundaries of evergreen forest stands	• Plantation of monoculture and introduced tree species → uniformity, loss of biodiversity
Clear felling	• Bare land after clear felling → water erosion → increased sediment and organic matter loads → eutrophication, sedimentation	• Bare land after clear felling → wind and water erosion • Use of vehicles → compaction • Sudden decrease in water demand following clear felling → waterlogging	• Large clearances → scarred landscapes	• If dead/decaying wood removed → loss of plant and animal species which depend on this → loss of biodiversity
Draining	• Lowering of groundwater level reducing water availability • Oxidation of organic soils → soil acidification → groundwater acidification	• Oxidation of organic soils → acid-sulphate formation → soil acidification	• Drying of land causing changes in plant communities and hence landscape	• Lowering of water table → loss of wet forests and wetlands high in biodiversity
Weeding, cleaning, thinning	• Use of herbicides → groundwater pollution	• Increased frequency of vehicle use → erosion and compaction	• Removal of greenery → uniformity	• Removal of understorey, an important habitat for many animal species → loss of biodiversity
Pesticide and fertiliser application	• Leaching of applied substances → groundwater pollution	• Fertilisation in waterlogged conditions → denitrification → greenhouse gas emission → contribution to climate change	• Changes in plant communities and hence landscapes	• Release of chemical pesticides → poisoning of non-target species • Fertiliser applications → changes in plant communities
Heavy machinery use	• Soil erosion → increased sediment load in surface waters • Oil leakage/spills → water pollution • Soil sealing → increased runoff, decreased infiltration to groundwater	• Increased frequency of vehicle use → soil compaction and erosion • Oil leakage/spills → soil pollution		• Increased frequency of vehicle use → disturbance of wildlife
Recreation	• Increased use of water → reduction of water availability and pollution through effluent from tourist centres, camping grounds, etc	• Trampling leading to erosion and compaction	• Infrastructure development (access roads, recreation centres, etc) → changes in landscape	• Increased number of visitors in forests → wildlife disturbance • Recreational infrastructure development → increased groundwater abstraction affecting tree growth
Hunting		• Soil contamination from lead pellets	• Reduced access to forest at hunting periods	• Removal of some animal species (eg, wolf, bear, lynx) from original range → loss of biodiversity • Selection of hunted species to other species detriment → loss of biodiversity • Poisoning of avifauna from lead pellets • Damage from overstocked game
Grazing and browsing	• Overdensity of grazing/browsing animals → soil erosion and compaction → increased sediment load, decreased infiltration to groundwater	• Overdensity of grazing/browsing animals → soil erosion and compaction	• Overdensity of grazing/browsing animals → erosion and changes in landscape	• Overgrazing and browsing (overpopulation of game) → damage to young plants, trees and habitats

Figure 5.31 *Environmental impacts of forestry*

Source: Europe's Environment, European Environment Agency, 1995

- linnet –36%
- reed bunting –45%
- skylark –53%
- corn bunting –62%
- tree sparrow –81%.

These declines in farmland bird populations have coincided with changes in agricultural practices. These include:

- the switch from spring to autumn sowing of arable crops, which has also led to a loss of winter stubble, which protects the soil from erosion and returns nutrients to the soil
- a move away from crop rotation and mixed farming to arable farming, with less variety of food supply and habitats
- an increase in the inputs of inorganic fertilisers and pesticides, which build up through the food chain, and can affect the success or otherwise of their eggs hatching
- the intensification of pasture management.

QUESTIONS

1 Briefly explain **three** differences between agricultural ecosystems and natural ones.

2 Study Figure 5.18 which shows the effects of deforestation.

What are the geographic consequences of deforestation?

URBAN ECOSYSTEMS

Urban habitats are very diverse, with a large variety of microhabitats (Figure 5.32). In addition, they are very unstable owing to severe human interference and disturbance. Urban ecosystems vary in terms of size and diversity. There are at least ten types of urban ecosystem:

- residential gardens
- industrial sites
- inner city derelict land
- green areas and open spaces
- cemeteries
- traffic corridors
- waste disposal areas
- copses
- fields
- water bodies.

Figure 5.32 Urban biogeography – Camley Lake, Kings Cross, London

The size, form and land-use pattern of urban areas varies with the age, site, function and the physical and cultural environment in which they have developed.

Flora and fauna

Most of the plant and animal species in urban areas have been introduced recently. There are relatively few indigenous (native) species. Urban areas are attractive for immigrant species because of the variety of microhabitats, creation of different and new habitats and reduced competition. A large proportion of animals in urban areas are scavengers and opportunistic generalists. Omnivorous (meat and vegetable eaters), surface feeding, nocturnal and crepuscular (twilight) animals have an advantage over others. Urban species diversity is increased by hybridisation and deliberate introductions. Urban fauna include foxes, hedgehogs, bats and squirrels, while birds include sparrows, pigeons and gulls. In some cases, as for example, South London, exotic species, such as parakeets have bred and formed colonies.

There are many important interactions between plants and animals in towns, and food webs can be quite complex. Figure 5.33 shows some of the relationships between different species which are typical of urban areas.

Birds in towns

Birds often thrive in towns because there are many trees, buildings and even nest boxes for them to breed in. In the country, many birds die of cold and starvation in a hard winter, but in towns food is often plentiful on bird tables and rubbish tips. The heat island effect (see Chapter 1) means that towns are often several degrees warmer than the nearby countryside, especially near heated buildings. Breeding cycles of wild birds are mainly controlled by day length, so the extra light in city centres enables some birds, especially sparrows and pigeons, to breed all the year round.

Trees in urban areas

Trees in dense woodland grow close together and compete for light, therefore they tend to be tall and slender with narrow canopies. By contrast, isolated trees in urban areas are not competing with each other for light, water and nutrients, so they do not grow as tall and the canopies spread wider. Isolated trees in exposed situations are more vulnerable to damage from the wind, so having a thicker and shorter trunk which provides stronger support, is an advantage.

The effect of pollution

Pollution has a significant effect on the flora and fauna in urban areas. Particulate matter (smoke), sulphur dioxide (SO_2), nitric oxide (NO), nitrogen dioxide (NO_2) and the mixture of chemicals present in 'acid rain' are in general toxic.

Competition	Both species compete for the same resources, e.g. light, water	Grass and daises on a lawn
Mutualism	An association which benefits both species and is essential to both	Algae, fungus and lichen; Nitrogen- fixing bacteria in clover roots
Commensualism	One species benefits from the presence of another which is unaffected	Moss benefits by living on a tree trunk
Antibiosis (Allelopathy)	One species inhibits others near it	Lichens and some conifers produce growth inhibitors
Parasitism	One species benefits and the other suffers	Mistletoe on trees; Dutch elm disease on elms
Predation	One species eats another	Spider preys on fly; ladybirds eat greenfly

Figure 5.33 *Relationships between species in an urban environment*
Source: Keene, J, 1988, Oxford ecology: a walk on the wild side, Witney Press

The biological effects of pollution include:
- stunted growth
- normally year round species becoming deciduous (the conifer being probably the most vulnerable)
- early leaf fall of deciduous species
- development of all but the fastest-growing species such as willow and birch, being suppressed at very high pollution levels
- lichen deserts at high levels of pollution
- the evolution of melanism (developing a darker pigmentation) in certain groups of animals (more particularly moths) as a result of air pollution.

Air pollution varies with the time of year and with the air pressure conditions. Concentration of pollutants may increase up to six times in winter because of temperature inversion trapping them over the city. In addition, plants do not remove many pollutants from the air in winter as they are dormant. Thus pollutants have the greatest effect on plants which do not die down or lose their leaves in winter, that is, evergreen trees, mosses and lichens are affected more seriously than deciduous ones.

Smoke and dust levels can be very high in industrial areas and this reduces photosynthesis significantly, especially in evergreen plants which may keep the same leaves for several years.

Much urban land is contaminated. In urban soils levels of lead can be up to twenty times the background level and it also accumulates in plants and animals. For example, earthworms may contain twice the level of lead found in the soils in which they live. Many pesticides that are used on verges, gardens and parks do not break down for many months, even years. Industrial waste may contaminate the soil in areas where spoil heaps are common. Rubbish tips may cover large areas near any urban settlement, and seepage of heavy metals and contaminants into the surrounding soil and water is a major problem.

Energy flow

Cities are predominantly detrital systems in that they produce more organic and inorganic waste material than can be biologically recycled, and which therefore has to be removed by one means or another (Figure 5.34).

Succession

Succession is the change in plant species over time. The first part of succession is colonisation. In built-up areas this is influenced by:
- **aspect** – south facing slopes or walls are warmer and drier whereas north facing ones are colder and damper
- **porosity** – pores hold more rainwater, so wood, brick and mortar are colonised more rapidly than asbestos, stone and metal
- **slope** – horizontal areas and gentle slopes accumulate debris, and rainwater drains away more slowly, hence soil may develop; steep slopes experience rapid run-off and are therefore dry
- **surface roughness** – plants cannot stick to smooth surfaces like metal and glass
- **levels of pollution** – high concentrations of lead may inhibit colonisation.

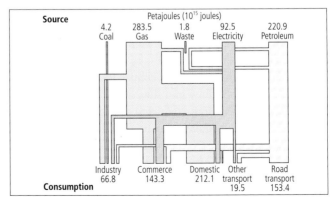

Figure 5.34 *Energy flow in an urban ecosystem – London, 1991*
Source: European Environment Agency, 1995, Europe's environment, European Environment Agency

As the soil deepens and nutrients increase, the number of species found also increases. A simple model of succession on a newly-exposed surface in an urban area might have six stages:

1 Lichens colonise the rock and produce acids which weather the rock and begin to form an embryonic soil.
2 If the material, for example a brick, is porous enough to hold water, or if some of the rock has weathered enough to hold water and soil particles, seeds of more advanced plants may colonise. Moss is common at this stage.
3 The dead moss and the minerals begin to form a soil. This provides stability, water and nutrients for the roots of more developed plants, such as groundsel, clover and annual grass. These plants, known as **ruderal** species, can survive on waste land, rubbish and debris. Plant succession is usually very rapid.
4 Rapidly growing annual plants are replaced by perennial grasses. Perennial herbs such as nettles and dandelions invade. They are longer living.
5 In time, dense thickets of bramble, hawthorn and elder develop. Small shrubs become established in cracks in the concrete, and the soil gets deeper. Ivy and bramble can outcompete the smaller plants and their roots can grow into deeper crevices in the rock.
6 Trees can only survive in deep soils, but on a wall trees such as yew can start to grow, although they tend to remain stunted.

Urban areas are a good place to look for evidence of succession. Derelict land, abandoned factories, railway cuttings, parks and open spaces can be found in many places.

The traditional view of succession is that it takes hundreds of years to occur because the breakdown of rock to form soil is very slow. Thus, in Britain, few urban areas will have seen much vegetation succession, or certainly will not have reached a climax community. However, a recent report (1996) believes that succession could be much more rapid than previously thought. It suggests that if cities were abandoned, weeds such as dandelions would become common within a year. This would start the process of urban succession. Grass and clover would cover level areas within about five years. Within a decade, soil would build up and deeper rooted trees and shrubs would take hold. Flooding would become more common as flood control would not be maintained. This would allow marshes and ponds to develop. Within thirty years, birch woodland would fill open spaces between buildings. Animal diversity would increase rapidly. However, some species would not survive. Sewer rats, for example, would not have people to provide for them. Only the more aggressive, adaptive animals, such as German Shepherd dogs, would survive.

Walls

Old walls have mostly rough surfaces and much of the mortar between the bricks is very old and porous. Before 1870 mortar was softer, being made of lime, loam, straw and sometimes cow dung. Modern mortar, made with Portland cement and sand, is harder and more resistant to weathering. In time, however, all mortar weathers and disintegrates – carbon dioxide in the air dissolves in rainwater to form a weak acid which weathers the cement. Increasingly acidic rainfall (from increased emissions of SO_2) speeds the disintegration of mortar. As the soluble products trickle away, insoluble sand and debris are left behind in cracks, forming the beginning of soil. Building stone, for example Cotswold limestone, weathers more slowly, so flowering plants will take root in the mortar region, not on the stone itself.

If the wall is damp enough, plant seeds or spores start to germinate. As their roots grow, they may force cracks to widen still further. Roots produce carbon dioxide which also help to weather the mortar. When the plant dies, it provides the developing soil with humus. The first plants to establish themselves are often quick growing annuals like groundsel and Oxford ragwort. Later, herbaceous plants (non-woody perennials) such as toadflax, snapdragon and red valerian appear. Finally, as the cracks enlarge, woody perennials such as buddleia and ivy grow. On some walls regular zoning can occur (Figure 5.35).

Some introduced plants, such as Oxford ragwort, are found in walls. Oxford ragwort is also found along wastelands beside railway lines as its light, airborne fruits are sucked along in the slipstream of passing trains. It colonised bombsites in the last war and is now common in walls and many disturbed areas, such as building sites, especially if they are rich in lime. Grazing animals avoid eating Oxford ragwort as it is toxic, therefore it can easily spread to become a pest. Herbicides will kill the plant, but of course it will also kill other things, including animals that might eat it. For this reason Oxford ragwort needs to be pulled up by hand.

- **Top zone –** drought evaders and succulents, for example ivy, Virginia creeper and clematis, tolerant to wind and bright light, often from fruits and seeds dropped by birds.
- **Upper zone –** differential expansion between coping and wall material result in cracking; overshadowing by the wall and higher plants lessens evaporation allowing rich growth, e.g. buddleia and Oxford ragwort.
- **Middle zone –** drier and barer. Lichens grow first, then mosses, ferns and flowering plants, e.g. ivy-leaved toadflax as mortar decays over a period of a century. Base moist because of splashes, capillary rise and overshadowing. If stone and plant litter accumulate, rich plant growth, for example nettles, develops.

Figure 5.35 Zonation of plants on a wall
Source: Keene, J., 1988, Oxford ecology: a walk on the wild side, Witney Press

	Natural	Agricultural
Foodweb	Complex; several layers	Simple; mostly one or two layers
Biomass	Large; mixed plant and animal	Small; mostly plant
Biodiversity	High	Low; often monoculture
Gene pool	High	Low, e.g. 3 species of cotton account for 53% of crop
Nutrient cycling	Slow; self-contained; unaffected by external supplies	Largely supported by external supplies
Productivity	High	Lower
Modification	Limited	Extensive – inputs of feed, seed, water, fertilisers, energy fuel; outputs of products, waste, etc.

Figure 5.36 *Ecosystems: natural and agricultural*
Source: Nagle, G., and Spencer, K., *Advanced geography revision handbook*, OUP

Aspect

The south-facing side of trees and stone and brickwork in the northern hemisphere tend to be more bare than the north-facing side because more solar radiation is received per unit area (Figure 5.37). Heat from the sun evaporates any water rapidly; the drought and the heat often make conditions too extreme for plants, apart from a few hardy lichens, to grow. Near the base of the tree or wall, where water can rise up the surface of the trunk, conditions will be damper, encouraging growth. On bark, stone and brick, the damper or north-facing side is often covered with mosses or the green microscopic single-celled algae, Pleurococcus. However, where trunks are shaded by other trees for most of the year, the south side will stay moist and also become green. Similarly, where water is prevented from trickling down the trunk by being sheltered by a branch, bark may be dry and bare even on the north side.

Wind also plays a part – the side of trees or walls facing the prevailing wind will be dried rapidly on a fine day but soaked by driving wind on a wet one. Hence there will be different species on different sides of a tree or wall, to exploit the difference in microclimate.

Grasslands in urban areas

A perfect lawn is an example of monoculture – all the plants except grasses have been eliminated. This is seldom achieved outside bowling greens, where hand weeding or use of herbicides kills any broad-leaved weeds. On any lawn frequent mowing soon eliminates plants which have their growing point at the top of the stem. Rosette plants like daisies, dandelions and plantain can survive, as the growing point is near the soil level and undamaged by close mowing.

If grass is mown less frequently and cuttings are not removed, conditions alter considerably. Taller plants can

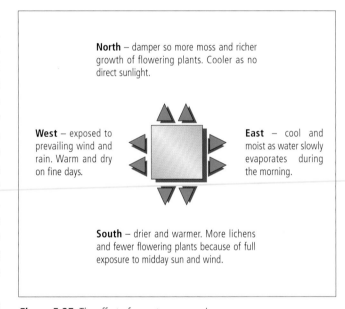

Figure 5.37 *The effect of aspect on succession*
Source: Keane, J., 1988, *Oxford ecology: a walk on the wild side*, Witney Press

survive and may seed. As the top of every plant is removed, the cuttings, often including seed head, are distributed evenly where they rot to enrich the ground and seeds are dispersed.

On sports fields, grass is mown and cuttings are left. Periodic and localised trampling occurs during matches and will affect some areas, and damage to the vegetation is greater near to things like the goal mouth. At the edge of paths, if there are railings, mowing is prevented and the soil is enriched by things such as bird droppings, fallen leaves, dog faeces, etc. As a result, the verges of fields and paths are often quite rich and include a rich herb layer, and there may even be the development of scrub vegetation (Figure 5.38, see page 106).

Figure 5.38 Urban grasslands

On footpaths, soil is compacted by trampling so none but the toughest plants can survive in the hard ground, and then only where trampling is minimal. Unlike mowing, trampling can damage even low growing plants. Some plants, however, such as annual meadow grass, silver thread moss and rosette plants like hawkbit, dandelion, and daisies, are remarkably tolerant to vertical pressure and abrasion caused by trampling.

Contrasting urban ecosystems

The city centre is, in some respects, a severe and stressful ecosystem. It includes:

- tall buildings
- very little soil material
- extreme variations in temperature, shade and shelter.

Open spaces may be few and far between, although some urban areas have large central parks. Many habitats are very small. They include roof top gardens, window boxes, trees on pavements, and areas where sufficient dust and debris can accumulate to form a soil.

For some species, however, urban environments offer an ideal habitat (Figure 5.39). Species which live in cliffs are ideally suited. Birds such as gulls, pigeons, sparrows and kestrels have expanded their numbers as they have adapted to urban environments. This has often included a change in diet to include garbage, small birds and insects.

Most mammals do not find it easy to adapt to urban environments. There are notable exceptions such as rats, mice, cats, dogs and grey squirrels.

By contrast, in residential suburbs there are a variety of planted and managed ecosystems. These include domestic gardens, school grounds, allotments, sports fields and cemeteries. Compared with the city centre, these provide:

- a greater range of habitats
- a larger food supply

Advantages

- Warmth – more animals and plants can survive in winter.
- Food – birds, squirrels and small mammals do not die of starvation or thirst in winter. Fewer birds need to migrate.
- Trees – a greater number of trees give nest sites, food and shelter to many animals.
- Shelter – buildings or bat boxes give safer breeding places.
- Light – birds breed for longer because of artificial light.
- Lack of pesticides – fewer bees, butterflies and other insects are killed.

Disadvantages

- Lack of soil – large areas are covered with roads and buildings.
- Pollution – due to the presence of cars and industries emitting noxious gases.
- Drought – due to rapid run-off and evaporation, or waterlogging because of soil compaction.
- Damage – due to mowing, trampling and vandalism.
- Lack of nutrients – removal of debris prevents natural recycling.
- Wind – in areas where buildings cause excessive turbulence.

Figure 5.39 Advantages and disadvantages of urban living
Source: Keane, J., 1988, Oxford ecology: a walk on the wild side, Witney Press

- more plant cover
- greater soil development.

Consequently, there is a larger range of animal and bird life in residential areas. As well as more breeding birds, mammals, such as foxes and hedgehogs, do well.

Another type of urban ecosystem is waste land. These areas may have:

- important variations in micro-relief
- a hard, impermeable surface
- mixed substrata including building rubble
- increased chemical loads.

These areas are the first to be colonised by ruderal species from the surrounding area. Plant succession is usually very rapid. In time the rapidly developing annual grasses are replaced by slower developing, but longer lasting perennial grasses. At a much later stage of succession, trees and shrubs such as bramble, hawthorn and elder are found.

QUESTIONS

1 What type of animals do you find in urban ecosystems?

2 How have they adapted to life in urban areas?

3 How and why does the microclimate of walls vary?

4 Describe briefly the process of colonisation of a bare surface in an urban area.

SUMMARY

In this chapter we have examined the basic functioning of ecosystems. We have seen how natural ecosystems are increasingly affected by human activity. In Britain, the main natural ecosystem is temperate deciduous woodland. However, there is relatively little left today. Instead, more and more forests are coniferous (because of the greater financial rewards). Other ecosystems, such as moorlands and heathlands are seen to be a result of human activities thousands of years ago. In Britain today, most of the land is used for agriculture. Agricultural ecosystems are quite impoverished compared with natural ones. Finally, in urban areas, there are a variety of ecosystems, which make small scale detailed investigations possible and rewarding.

QUESTIONS

1 Describe the interrelationships of climate, soils and vegetation in an urban ecosystem.
2 How do urban ecosystems differ from natural ones?
3 Describe and explain the variety of ecosystems that can be found in a relatively small area, such as a school and its grounds.
4 Using the Skills section 'Writing about ecosystems' describe and explain the characteristics of an urban ecosystem. Use the following paragraph headings:
   • location or example
   • climate
   • soils (see pages 67-83)
   • vegetation
   • energy flows
   • nutrient cycles
   • animals
   • any unique local conditions.

EXTENDED (PROJECT) WORK

Investigating urban ecosystems
For a small area, such as in your school grounds or in your neighbourhood, investigate some of the following:
1 Bare walls
   • Do flowering plants grow on building stone or brick surfaces or on the mortar?
   • Compare rough rock surfaces with smooth rock surfaces; new mortar with old mortar; the brick of a garden wall with the brick of a house wall, and the stone of a garden wall with the stone of a house wall.
   • What are the main problems facing animals and plants on a south facing wall?
   • How might a north west or east facing wall differ?
   • What advantages are there for animals living on a south facing wall?
   • What problems do plants have here that they do not have elsewhere?
   • How do these plants arrive here in the first place?

2 Urban woodlands
   • Is the trunk of a tree greener on the north side compared to the south or west side (the same is true of walls, roofs and bridges)?
   • What factors govern the distribution of algae, moss and lichen on tree trunks?

3 Grassland
   • Compare the variety of different plants in different areas, for example on a lawn, on the edge of a footpath, in the footpath, in an area of meadow land, on a sports field.
   • What controls the type of plant found in each type of area?
   • What factors account for the differences in the height of the plants?

4 Hedges
   • How does an urban hedge differ from a rural hedge?
   • What species are found in urban hedges?
   • What species are found in rural hedges?

Investigating woodlands
Describe the height, type, diversity, density and structure of woodland vegetation (Figure 5.39). For example:
   • What type of trees are present?
   • How many different types of trees are present?
   • How many layers are there in the vegetation?
   • What species make up the tree (or canopy) layer?
   • What species make up the shrub layer?
   • What species make up the field layer?
   • What vegetation is found on the ground layer?

   • Describe the thickness and the composition of the litter layer.
   • What type of soil is found there? Use Chapter 4 for methods to investigate soils.

BIBLIOGRAPHY AND RECOMMENDED READING

Collins, M., 1984, *Urban ecology*, Cambridge University Press
European Environment Agency, 1995, *Europe's environment*, EEA
HMSO, 1994, *Biodiversity; The UK action plan*, HMSO
Keane, J., 1988, *Oxford ecology: a walk on the wild side*, Witney Press
MacArthur, R. and Wilson, E., 1967, *The theory of island biogeography*, Princeton University Press
Mills, S., 1987, *Nature in its place*, The Bodley Head
Tivy, J., 1993, *Biogeography*, Longman
Wilcove, D et al., 1986, Habitat Fragmentation in the Temperate Zone, in **Soule, M.** (Ed), *Conservation biology: the science of scarcity and diversity*, Sinauer

WEB SITES

The Rainforest Action Network Home Page - http://www.ran.org/ran/
EnviroLink Home Page - http://www.envirolink.org/index1.html
The Natural History Museum - http://www.nhm.ac.uk/index2.html
Infoseek: Planet Earth - http://guide-p.infoseek.com/
New Scientist: Planet Science - http://www.newscientist.com/

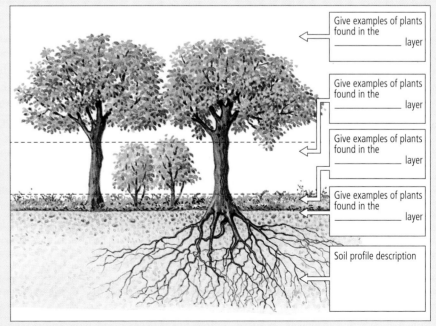

Give examples of plants found in the _____ layer

Give examples of plants found in the _____ layer

Give examples of plants found in the _____ layer

Give examples of plants found in the _____ layer

Soil profile description

Figure 5.39 *Structure of a woodland ecosystem*

Chapter 6
Managing environments

The previous chapters have looked at some of the ways in which Britain's environment is changing. Some of this is due to natural forces, but much is due to human activity. Many of these changes have had a negative impact upon the environment, although there are increasing attempts to reverse the trend and make improvements to the environment. In this final chapter we look at some of the ways in which the environment is protected and managed. We look at National Parks in Britain and Ireland, coastal management by the National Trust, and management of erosion risk at the Giant's Causeway, Northern Ireland.

ENVIRONMENTAL PROTECTION ORGANISATIONS

In the British Isles there are a number of organisations, bodies and pieces of legislation that protect natural and cultural landscapes. These include National Parks, Areas of Outstanding Natural Beauty (AONBs), Heritage Coasts, Sites of Special Scientific Interest, Environmentally Sensitive Areas, World Heritage Sites and National Scenic Areas (NSAs). National Parks, AONBs and NSAs account for about 22% of the UK (Figure 6.3). In the Republic of Ireland, National Parks are an important conservation tool and account for about 2% of the landscape.

National Park	Residents (thousands)	Visitor days (millions)
Peak District	40.0	20.0
Dartmoor	33.0	8.5
Lake District	40.0	20.0
Snowdonia	25.0	9.0
North York Moors	25.0	11.0
Pembrokeshire coast	22.0	8.0
Exmoor	10.0	2.5
Yorkshire Dales	18.6	9.5
Northumberland	2.5	1.0
Brecon Beacons	32.0	7.0

Figure 6.1 Residents and visitors in the National Parks
Source: Countryside Commission, 1992

The ten National Parks in England and Wales were designated in 1955 as a result of the 1949 National Parks and Access to the Countryside Act. This defined National Parks as extensive tracts of country of great natural beauty which provided opportunities for outdoor recreation. The Act identified the need to enhance as well as preserve 'natural beauty', suggesting that areas worthy of protection should be conserved, maintained and enhanced. It also recognised that the 'needs of agriculture and forestry and the economic and social needs of rural areas' must be accommodated. This requirement created a breeding ground for conflict (Figure 6.2), and potentially, environmental disaster.

Figure 6.2 Conflict between enhancing natural beauty and the needs of tourism

The ten National Parks cover 1.4 million hectares, about 9% of the UK. In addition, there are two other large areas which receive special protection: the Norfolk Broads and the New Forest. The Broads is an important area in terms of its unique landscape and the recreational pressures it experiences. The New Forest comprises unenclosed woodland, heath and bog and also experiences severe pressure from visitors.

National Parks are now managed by the National Parks Authority (NPA), which is composed of local boards, committees and county councils. One-third of the authority is appointed by the government. However, much of the land in National Parks is privately owned by farmers and other individuals.

The duties of the NPA include:
- to persuade landowners to provide access for the public
- to plant woodlands
- to set up information centres
- to provide car parks and picnic sites.

In addition, there are 39 AONBs which account for about two million hectares or 13% of the UK land area. AONBs are smaller than the National Parks and offer fewer opportunities for outdoor recreation. Forty-four heritage coasts, which account for nearly one-third of the coastline, give protection to narrow belts along the shoreline. In Scotland, forty NSAs cover a large part of the west of the country.

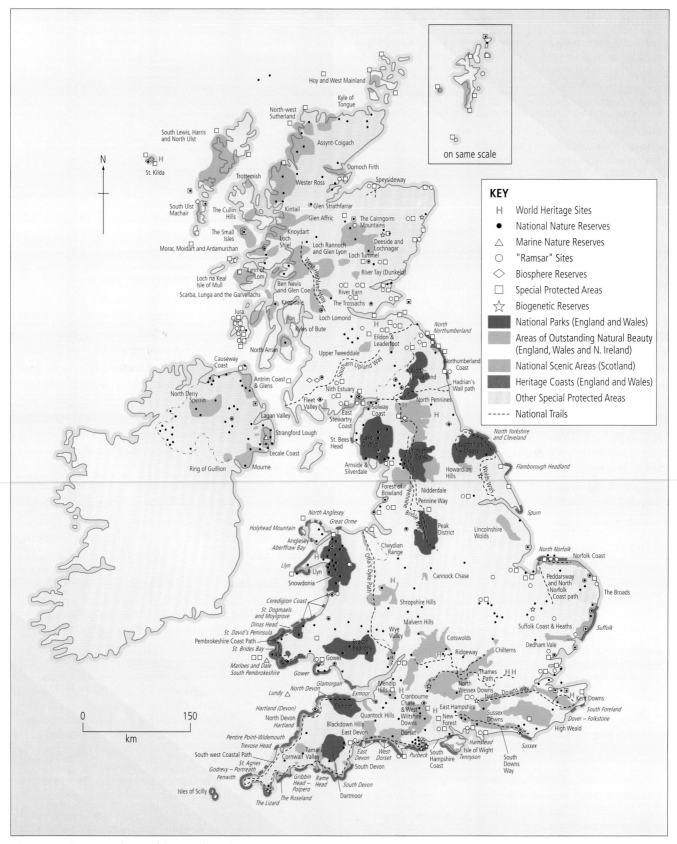

Figure 6.3 *The protected areas of the United Kingdom*

Source: Countryside Commission, English Nature, Department of National Heritage, Institute of Terrestrial Ecology, Department of the Environment, Countryside Council for Wales, Scottish National Heritage, Department of the Environment - Northern Ireland, 1997, Regional trends 32

Category	Number	Area (000s ha)
National Nature Reserves	286	172.5
Local Nature Reserves	241	17.1
Sites of Special Scientific Interest	5671	1788.5
Areas of Scientific Interest	46	63.4
Areas of Special Scientific Interest	26	6.9
Special Protection Areas	40	134.4
Biosphere Reserves	13	44.3
'Ramsar' Wetland Sites	44	133.7
Environmentally Sensitive Areas	19	785.6

Figure 6.4 *Statutory protected areas, UK*
Source: HMSO, Biodiversity, HMSO

At a much smaller scale, National Nature Reserves (NNRs) and Sites of Special Scientific Interest (SSSIs), provide local protection (Figure 6.4). Many of these are within National Parks and AONBs.

In the National Parks and the AONBs, development rights are more restricted than in other areas. This is not to say that developments are prohibited; planning permission is required, but, in some cases, the guidelines regulating planning permission are much tighter than in areas which are not National Parks or AONBs.

The conflicting interests of users of Dartmoor National Park is a good example of the general problems in National Parks. The Park receives over 8 million visits each year and this creates many tensions (Figure 6.5), in addition to conflicting land uses in the Park. The varied interest groups in the Dartmoor National Park include farmers, landlords, water authorities, the Forestry Commission, the National Trust, the Ministry of Defence, County Councils, residents and tourists.

Figure 6.5 *The conflict on Dartmoor*
Source: Nagle, G., 1998, Geography through diagrams, OUP

Figure 6.6 *The Yorkshire Dales National Park – contrast between moorland and fertile vales*

THE YORKSHIRE DALES NATIONAL PARK

The Yorkshire Dales are an excellent example of the conflicts between recreation and other uses. They are well known for their bare and open hills which descend into the contrasting terrain of fertile vales (Figure 6.6). The Yorkshire Dales was the seventh of the ten National Parks to be designated. It includes an area of about 1740 square kilometres including Dentdale, Garsdale and the southern Howgill Fells, Swaledale, Wensleydale, Upper Wharfedale and their tributary dales, and Upper Ribblesdale with the headwaters of the Aire in Malhamdale and the Greta valley in the Ingleborough area (Figure 6.7).

The Local Government Act of 1972 required National Park authorities to prepare a National Park Plan 'formulating their policy for the management of the Park'. In response, the Yorkshire Dales National Park Committee adopted a number of principles (Inset 6.1, see page 112).

Tourism brings in a great deal of money but creates noise, litter and pollution. The Dartmoor NPA tries to reduce the conflict by land-use zoning which attracts visitors to some areas (by providing car parks and other facilities) and keeps them away from other places (by not providing facilities).

Dartmoor is also used by the army. This causes soil erosion (by tanks) and disturbance to many birds and animals due to the firing ranges on Dartmoor. On the other hand, the Ministry of Defence keeps large areas free from visitors, so valuable landscapes are protected.

Demands for recreation include water sports, walking, pony-treking, mountain biking, hang gliding and bird watching. All of these require more facilities and improved access roads, leading to more pollution.

Dartmoor National Park receives over 8 million visits each year

The bedrock is granite, which is hard and impermeable and makes a good site for reservoirs, but they drown natural habitats.

Population growth in small towns and rural areas, and migration of retired people to the south west increases demand for housing, which increases demand for building materials, and also leads to the provision of more roads.

Afforestation schemes usually replace deciduous woodland with coniferous woodland but coniferous woodlands lack diversity compared to deciduous ones. For example, oak trees support about 400 types of insect whereas spruce trees support only three.

Farming has an impact on the environment. Overstocking causes vegetation removal and soil erosion.

China clay is mined from granite for industry. Quarries need access roads and are heavily polluted by dust and noise, spoil heaps and water pollution.

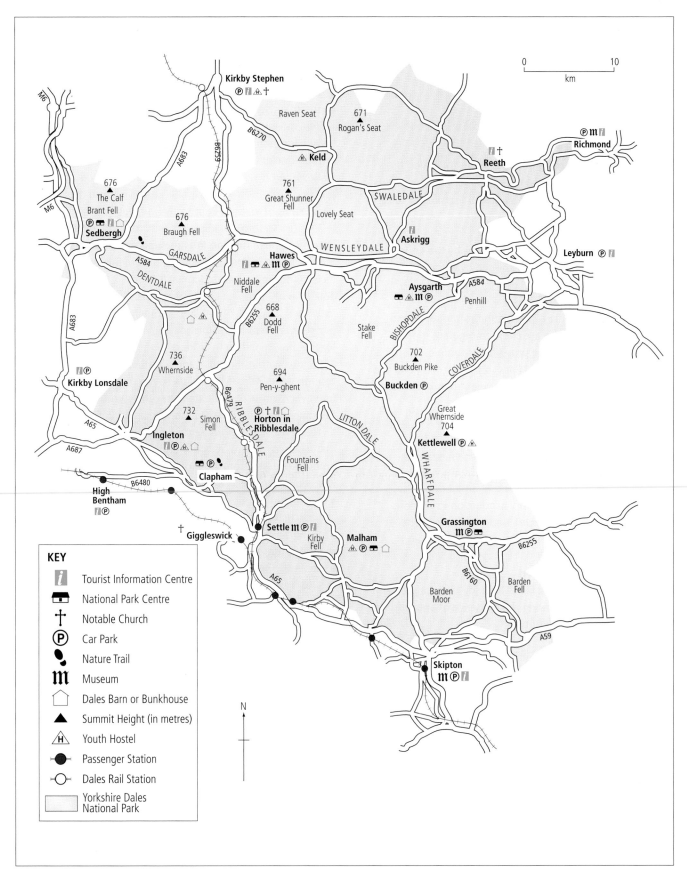

Figure 6.7 The Yorkshire Dales National Park

Source: *Conference of National Park Authorities, 1988, Managing the Dales through partnership, CNPAs*

Inset 6.1
Principles for managing the Yorkshire Dales

1 Landscape change
To ensure that as change takes place in the Dales, the landscape evolves without losing its special character, its high standard of scenery or its special features of cultural and scientific interest.

2 Landscape enhancement
To enhance the landscape of the Dales by the enrichment of its natural beauty, and by the removal and mitigation of disfigurements.

3 Social and economic needs
To give every possible consideration to the social and economic needs of the area, and to regulate the recreational uses and the provision of facilities for public enjoyment of the National Park so that farming and the social and economic life of the resident population are not dislocated or impaired.

4 Public understanding
To promote a better understanding between town and country by giving townspeople a deeper comprehension of the significance of nature, an appreciation of country lore and an insight into the essential processes of primary production in which country people are engaged, and to associate local people with the purposes of the National Park and to enlist their goodwill.

5 Access and accommodation
To enable visitors to the Dales to enjoy the qualities of natural beauty by ensuring the existence of appropriate access and accommodation.

6 Recreational activities
To ensure that recreational activities in the Dales are compatible, and that each is practised in such manner and by such means as will leave the natural beauty unimpaired for this and future generations.

Source: Yorkshire Dales National Park, 1984, National Park Plan

In a recent comprehensive survey of visitors to the Park, a number of key results were found:

- over 6 million people visit the Dales each year (see Figure 6.1 page 108) The Countryside Commission states that over 9 million visitor days are spent in the Dales – this is found by multiplying the number of visitors by the average length of stay
- August is the peak month with almost 20% of visitors
- the peak day is August Bank holiday with over 80 000 visitors
- the largest attraction is Wharfedale with over 493 000 visitors per year
- 86% of visitors used cars for their visit to the Dales
- the majority of visitors were day visitors.

The most popular activity was found to be sightseeing, followed by picnicking and exploring villages. Of the active pursuits, walking was by far the most popular. Up to 50% of visitors had a walk – 27% of all visitors walked over 8 kilometres and 23% between 3 and 8 kilometres. A high proportion of visitors kept to the villages or their cars!

Visitors to the Yorkshire Dales National Park bring many benefits. These include jobs to support the tourist industry, income spent in the area, the support of facilities available to local communities, and increased choice of shops in the area. Total visitor spending in the Yorkshire Dales National Park is estimated at about £46 million annually. A further £14 million per year is spent by visitors staying outside the park who visit for the day. Spending by visitors to the Park supports a total of 1505 jobs within the park, and a further 355 in the areas surrounding the Dales. Many of these are part-time and seasonal, however, and it is estimated that the number of equivalent full-time jobs are 989 within the Park and 256 outside it.

However, visitors also bring problems: physical damage, disturbance to farm livestock and wildlife, congestion, development pressure on the landscape and social pressures on local communities. These pressures include:

- honeypot sites – increased numbers of visitors causes destruction to the sites they come to see
- visitors want car parks, visitor centres, and other facilities
- congestion leads to noise and air pollution
- second homes cause an increase in local house prices, and a decline in housing for local people
- landowners – do not like people roaming over their land
- crops may get trampled on, gates may be left open
- agricultural developments remove dry stone walls, heathlands, hedgerows, meadows and woodlands
- excessive commercialisation.

In the survey, residents and visitors to the Dales considered that the Dales were changing. 48% of residents and 34% of visitors thought that the Dales were declining in their attractiveness.

Agriculture in the Dales

Farming has helped shape the Dales landscape and remains an important source of employment and income for many people. A difficult climate, with cold winters, high levels of rainfall and a limited growing season, and varying topography combine to create a farming economy mostlybased on grass. However, a number of changes in agricultural practice are affecting the landscape of the Dales. For example, increasing use of chemical fertilisers and herbicides has made lowland grasslands more fertile and more productive, but less valuable for wildlife compared with fields managed in a traditional way. In the traditional hay meadows and pastures there were more habitats for wildlife and a greater variety of grasses and flowering plants. Manuring by grazing stock helped raise soil fertility. By contrast, the use of chemical fertilisers favours perennial grasses, which can survive through the winter and receive nutrients from the soil.

Drainage of the land has been a form of land management for many centuries. The main methods used were 'moorland gripping' or under drainage and tile drainage. Moorland gripping involves the creation of open ditches to drain away surface water and excess water in the soil. Under drainage involves the laying of pipes through the soil to achieve the same effect as tile drainage. In the Dales, because of thin soils, under drainage is not always possible. Ditches cause a number of problems:
- very rapid run-off
- increased risk of flash floods on lower ground
- a decline in the extent of natural moorlands.

Dry stone walls are a characteristic feature of the Yorkshire Dales. They were built at a time when materials and labour were in plentiful and cheap supply. Now, however, materials are more scarce and labour is more expensive so wire fencing and posts are commonly used instead. Even in areas where hedges are common, they are increasingly being replaced by wire and posts.

Nearly 30% of the Dales is common land (no one person owns it but many people have use of it). Most of this common land is moorland. These areas have particular problems:
- overall responsibility is difficult to establish
- changes in grazing practices lead to landscape and vegetation changes
- unrestricted public access rights are thought to exist
- the grass and heather areas suffer from under-management and are of poor quality.

The traditional Dales landscape of patchwork fields containing small barns is changing. In the traditional labour intensive system of farming, a large number of small barns for storing fodder and housing sick or weak animals was an efficient way of managing herds. Those barns which remain are in need of much repair. In some instances they have been converted to cheap, low cost holiday accommodation. As a result of changes in agriculture, many traditional barns are too small. The general aim of the NPA is that new farm buildings should fit their surroundings. However, stone to build barns in the traditional way is in short supply and is also expensive, so cheaper, visually intrusive materials are used. In some cases new buildings may be considered an eyesore but the NPA has no direct control over their removal.

Figure 6.8 *The effects of quarrying*

Quarrying in the Dales

Mining is a traditional activity in the Dales. There are a number of important mines such as those at Giggleswick, Horton-in-Ribblesdale, Kilnsey, Threshfield, and Wharfedale (all limestone), and gritstone at Helwith Bridge and Ingleton.

Existing quarries cause varying degrees of visual intrusion; the effect is especially marked in Ribblesdale and Wharfedale (Figure 6.8). The quarries also affect cave systems, archaeological remains, SSSIs and agricultural activities.

QUESTIONS

1 What are the attractions of the Yorkshire Dales National Park?

2 Using an atlas, find out which large urban areas are within 80 kilometres of the Yorkshire Dales National Park.

3 Explain why traffic congestion is a major problem in the Dales.

4 Explain how changing agricultural practices are affecting the landscape of the Dales.

5 Briefly outline the problems in balancing development and management in the Yorkshire Dales National Park.

STUDLAND BEACH, DORSET

Studland Beach is an excellent example of a coastal area where the needs of recreation and the environment are closely managed (Figure 6.9, see page 114).

Studland Beach is still wild and largely unspoilt. It is fronted by the broad sandy beaches of Shell Bay and Studland Bay, behind which are a succession of sand dune ridges and slacks (low lying areas between the sand dunes) leading to heathland, woodland, marsh and a large freshwater lake, the Little Sea. Because of the rich and varied plant and animal life, the area was declared a National Nature Reserve in 1962.

The National Trust tries to run Studland Beach as a family beach, and the numbers of visitors are controlled by price of parking and limiting the car parking spaces available. Since the National Trust became responsible for the beach in

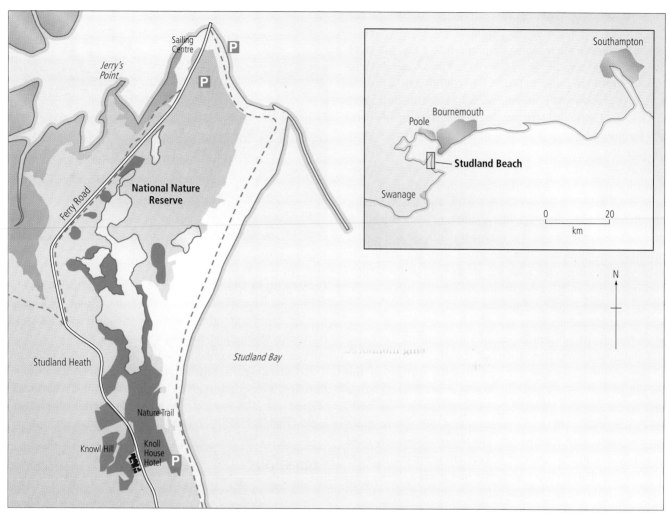

Figure 6.9 *Studland Beach*
Source: O.S. map

1992, it has increased the capacity for car parking by the provision of an overflow car park that can take a maximum of 500 cars. A Visitor Centre was built in 1990 at the Knoll Car Park. It includes a shop, cafe and information point. There are 311 beach huts situated along the front of the beach. The majority of these are privately owned, but the Trust manages 38 for weekly and seasonal lets.

There are a number of problems in the management of Studland Beach.

1 There are four car parks in Studland, plus two overflow parks. The capacity on a busy day, with cars moving in and out, is 3500 cars. In addition, on a busy day there can be up to 1000 cars parked along the Ferry Road and as many as 300 cars parked illegally on yellow lines in the village. During the season, Easter to the end of September, the total number of cars in National Trust parks is 140 000–200 000.

2 Visitors are in excess of 1 000 000 per year. They are mostly concentrated in July and August. Estimated numbers of visitors on the beach on a busy day are 20 000-25 000, with approximately 8000 coming across by foot on the Bournemouth/Studland chain ferry. Of all the visitors, about 95% come just for the beach, and only 5% venture into the Nature Reserve.

3 Large volumes of litter, 12–13 tonnes a week, are dumped on the beach by the visitors. To cope with the problem, the National Trust puts out approximately 200 litter bins (emptied daily) during the summer months.

4 Large numbers of lost children, often up to 30 a day, have to be reunited with their parents. (Once on the beach, most areas of the beach and dunes look very similar, so it is very easy to get lost.)

5 There are conflicts between naturists and walkers along the coastal path, between power boat enthusiasts and dinghy sailors, between board sailers, swimmers and sun-bathers, and between local dog walkers and visitors. The main conflict of interest is between naturists and walkers. People using the coastal path for walking, feel offended by the naturists. So a new footpath, called Heather Walk, has been created. It runs behind the naturist area in the

Figure 6.10 *Visitor pressure on Studland Beach*

dunes, allowing the general public to walk the full length of the beach without encountering naturists.

6 There is some wear and tear on the footpaths on the Nature Reserve (Figure 6.10), but this is being monitored and walkways of wooden duckboards have been put down in the most worn parts.

Visitor numbers	Over 1 000 000 per year
Parking spaces	About 3500 in National Trust parks
	1000 on the roadside of Ferry road
	300 on the verges around the village
Total number of cars per year in National Trust parks	135 000-210 000
Foot passengers during the High Season on the Ferry on a busy day	8000
Estimated numbers of visitors to the beach on busy day	20 000-25 000
Number of cars using the car parks	
1992	138 430
1993	142 643
1994	158 949
1995	178 228
1996	150 880
The spread of visitors over 1996	
Jan to June (33%)	49 668
July and August (58%)	87 699
September (9%)	13 513

Figure 6.11 *Visitors to Studland Beach*
Source: National Trust, 1997, Studland Beach and dunes, environmental management of a popular coastal site

EROSION AT THE GIANT'S CAUSEWAY, N. IRELAND

The Giant's Causeway is one of the most remarkable landscapes in the British Isles. As a result, it attracts many visitors. But it is an active coastline, and subject to much mass movement. Consequently, management is required.

The causeway, on the north coast of Northern Ireland, is famous for its geology and geomorphology, its cliffs and its rare plant environments. As a result it attracts over 370 000 visitors each year. This creates a great strain on the attractions that the visitors come to see – the cliffs and the headlands – and in addition, the paths that give them access to the sites.

The Causeway Coast has been designated a World Heritage Site by UNESCO, largely as a result of its unique geological formations – the hexagonal columns of basalt formed by the rapid cooling of lava when it reached the sea millions of years ago. In addition, it is classified as a National Nature Reserve and an Area of Outstanding Natural Beauty. These titles recognise the importance of the Causeway Coast and confirm that management is essential to maintain its character. However, the designations also reflect the pressure that the area experiences as a result of visitor numbers.

One of the main problems is that of footpath erosion. The public footpath network (Figure 6.12, see page 116) provides easy access to the Causeway, bays and headlands and gives some dramatic views of the area. These paths have been developed over a period of about 150 years, and now consist of two main routes, and a number of smaller ones.

The erosion of the footpaths has been the result of natural processes combined with human pressure. Erosion from natural causes, such as wave action, freeze-thaw weathering and landslides occurs mostly in winter. Landslides are common along most of the stretch but are especially common on the headlands (Figure 6.13, see page 116). These landslides are related to the high rates of wave erosion on the flanks of the headland which destabilise the slopes above.

As a result of the severe erosion and consequent instability of the area, the footpaths have become hazardous. The condition of the footpaths is determined by two factors:
- the nature of the footpath itself, including whether it is even, deeply rutted, safe to walk on
- the position of the footpath in the landscape, for example, at the top of a cliff, or at the base of a cliff.

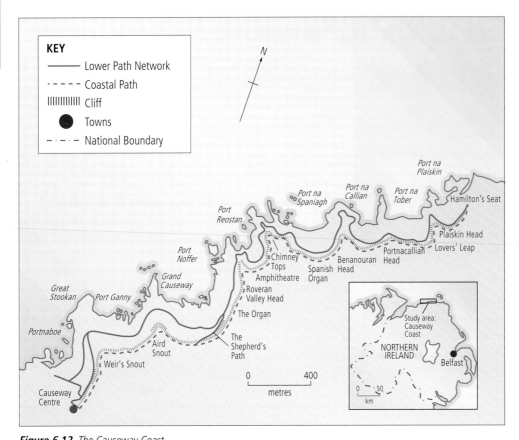

Figure 6.12 *The Causeway Coast*

Source: Smith, B. and Ferris, C., 1997, Giant's Causeway: management of erosion hazard,
Geography reveiew, 11, 1, 30-37

Figure 6.13 *Mass movements between the
Chimney Tops and Benanouran headlands*

Source: Smith, B. and Ferris, C., 1997, Giant's Causeway: management of erosion hazard, Geography reveiew, 11, 1, 30-37

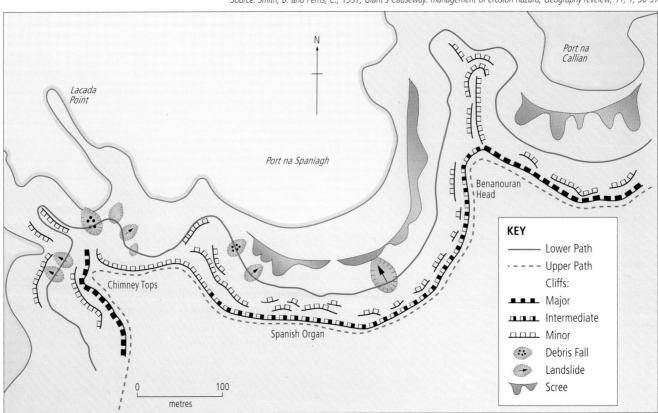

The Causeway authorities have developed a four fold classification of risk:

1 least hazardous areas – including places where the path runs along a flat surface with no cliff or scree slope on the seaward side; the landward side is overlooked by small cliffs and/or debris slopes

2 hazardous – seaward edges are close to steep (>40°) cliffs but landward they are overlooked by minor cliffs

3 very hazardous – seaward edges are close to steep (>40°) cliffs and landward they are overlooked by steep (>40°) slopes

4 extremely hazardous (Figure 6.12) – seaward edges are close to steep (>40°) cliffs and landward they are overlooked by steep (>40°) slopes which continuously shed debris and are subject to major slope failures.

The Chimney Tops headland is particularly subject to mass movements (Figure 6.13). In some sections the paths have become so unsafe that they have been closed. The area from The Spanish Organ to Port na Spaniagh is important for visitors as it gives some of the best views of the coastline and provides experience of walking the cliffs. However, the path is subject to rock falls and landslides. The path from Port na Spaniagh eastwards to Hamilton's Seat is also very hazardous and subject to active slope failure (Figure 6.14 and 6.15). It is subject to rock falls, landslides and complete collapse of parts of the cliff. The lower path between Port na Spaniagh and Hamilton's Seat has been closed to the public since 1994 after landslides removed part of the path and covered other parts of the path with debris.

There are a number of techniques which could have been used to stabilise the coastline, such as pinning the slope, or spraying it with concrete (to 'glue' the slope) or providing wire meshes to catch the falling rocks. However, these are visually disruptive and are not compatible with the status of a heritage coast and with protecting the Causeway's wide variety of habitats. Hence the decision was taken to close the

Figure 6.15 *Landslide on the Giant's Causeway Coast*

lower footpath; the measure has proved quite successful. There was little opposition to the plan since only about 8% of visitors used the path before it was closed. Closure of that part of the path network has been balanced by investment and upgrading of other areas. There is now a clear policy of educating visitors to appreciate the nature of the Causeway coastline and there are more sign posts and viewing areas.

QUESTIONS

1 Using an atlas, explain why Studland Beach attracts more visitors each year than the Giant's Causeway.

2 Briefly outline the attractions of the Causeway Coast.

3 Why are mass movements such a hazard on the Chimney Tops headland?

4 Identify the types of mass movement on Figure 6.13, a geomorphological map of the area.

5 In what ways is it easier to manage an area such as the Causeway coastline compared to the beach at Studland?

KILLARNEY NATIONAL PARK, REPUBLIC OF IRELAND

Killarney National Park is an excellent example of land-use management in an area renowned for its scenic beauty. However, the region relies heavily on tourism as a source of employment and revenue and, as the amount of paid holidays, disposable income and transport infrastructure has increased or improved, the number of tourists visiting Killarney has risen dramatically. Conflicts between environment and the economy have intensified but the management policy in Killarney National Park illustrates how tourism and conservation can be successfully managed: by placing the emphasis firmly on conservation.

The scenery of the Killarney area in Eire, including the National Park, is world renowned. It is a major attraction and the area is one of the most visited tourist venues in Ireland (Figure 6.15). Over a million visitors travel to County Kerry each year, bringing an estimated £160 million to the area. Of these, the majority visit Killarney, a town with a resident population of 7275 and over 8000 tourist bed spaces!

Figure 6.14 *A footpath damaged by a landslide on the Causeway coastline*

Figure 6.16 Killarney National Park, Ireland

Since the local economy is so heavily dependent on tourism, the Park must continue to cater for the needs of tourists by providing and maintaining the facilities necessary for visitor enjoyment. This is not always environmentally beneficial. However, under legislation in Ireland, where conflict arises between the needs of tourism against the need for conservation, the protection of the natural heritage takes precedence.

The Victorian poet Alfred Austin wrote about Killarney that 'if mountain wood and water harmoniously blent constitute the most perfect and adequate loveliness that nature presents, it surely must be owned that it has, all the world over, no superior'. The scenic quality of Killarney comes from a variety of physical and human landscapes (Figure 6.16). It includes the three lakes of Killarney; secluded lake shores, sometimes with low limestone cliffs; rocks and islands; waterfalls, tarns and rapidly flowing rivers; rugged sandstone mountains with moorland and some bare rock surfaces; glacially eroded valleys; native oak woodlands; the last herd of native red deer in Ireland; landscaped grasslands; historic buildings and bridges, cottages and monastic and religious ruins.

Killarney National Park is managed by the Office of Public Works (OPW) in accordance with international criteria set down by IUCN, the World Conservation Union. The Park is included in the United Nations List of National Parks and Equivalent Reserves and has been designated a Biosphere Reserve by UNESCO.

A concise definition of National Parks in Eire is given as areas which 'exist to conserve natural plant and animal communities and scenic landscapes which are both extensive and of national importance and, under conditions compatible with that purpose, to enable the public to visit and appreciate them'.

The five basic objectives for the National Park are:
- to conserve nature
- to conserve other significant features and qualities
- to encourage public appreciation of the heritage and the need for conservation
- to develop a harmonious relationship between the Park and the community
- to enable the Park to contribute to science through environmental monitoring and research.

Of these, nature conservation takes precedence over the others should any conflict arise. Unlike Britain, where National Parks contain large rural communities and there is pressure on the environment from agriculture and rural dwellers, Irish National Parks are practically free of inhabitants and farming activities. Hence the conservation can be made a priority.

Management strategy in the Park

Nevertheless, Killarney National Park is not without its problems. It does not comprise a self-contained ecological unit, consequently it is influenced by changes and developments which take place in the surrounding area. To successfully manage the interests of conservation and tourism, Killarney National Park has developed a management plan in which land use is controlled and compromises are made between conflicting uses. The Killarney National Park Management

Plan identifies four zones (Figure 6.17):

1 Natural zone: where nature conservation is the primary objective
2 Cultural zone: where the primary objective is the conservation of noteworthy features resulting from human activities, including demesne (country estate) landscapes, archaeological and historic sites, buildings and structures
3 Intensive management zone: where basic objectives other than conservation are emphasised, provided Park resources are not adversely affected
4 Resource restoration zone: comprising conifer plantations, mainly in the Muckross area.

In addition, the management plan identifies a potential Buffer Zone around the Park within which development and change will be influenced in a positive manner. This has been developed in consultation with Kerry County Council, Killarney Urban District Council and other relevant bodies.

Within the National Park itself, there are a number of priorities which the Park authorities have been tackling. Control and eradication of the rhododendron population is perhaps the biggest conservation challenge facing the National Park. (Rhododendrons are very dense shrubs which grow rapidly and shade out native species, thus leading to the decline of biodiversity.) Up to 900 hectares of the Park's 11 200 hectares of native woodland are infested with rhododendrons. Approximately 240 hectares have been cleared and the aim is to achieve the clearance of 75% of the infested woodland and to maintain the cleared areas. The second aim is the removal of forestry plantations situated in the Resource Restoration Zone. Here the aim is to replace most of the plantations with natural vegetation and ultimately to integrate these areas into the other zones of the Park, principally the Natural Zone.

Development plans have been established for much of the built fabric of the Park. Muckross House is a late nineteenth-century mansion containing folk-life exhibits, craft workshops and a National Park interpretation of life in the mansion over the years. A folk farm has also been developed. There are plans to redesign the Park entrance in conjunction with Kerry County Council's plans to widen the main access road (N71) in this area. The former Kenmare Demesne, situated close to the town of Killarney, has plans for a major tree planting programme, restoration of internal pathways, development of car-parking areas, landscaping of the area and restoration of many formal features adja-

cent to the house and farmyard complex. Ross Castle has been reopened to the public on completion of the restoration works. A development programme has also been undertaken improving car-parking, toilet and boating facilities, landscaping and an information service for visitors. There are also plans to develop the long-distance footpaths in the area, such as the Kerry Way. The feasibility of a path around Lough Leane is also being examined.

Killarney National Park illustrates how tourists can be managed in an ecologically sensitive area. On the one hand they bring in much needed money and generate employment in the area, on the other hand they can cause serious problems such as traffic congestion, erosion of footpaths, destruction of vegetation and the ruin of scenic views through the provision of tourist amenities. The Killarney National Park has developed a plan which reconciles these, yet at the same time gives priority to the conservation of nature.

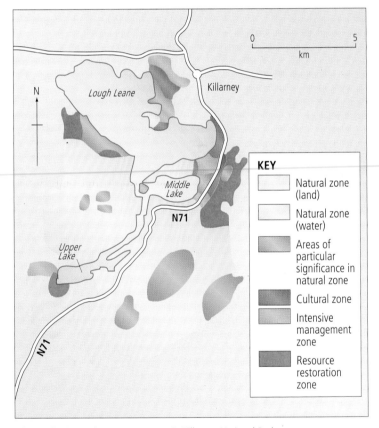

Figure 6.17 *Land-use management in Killarney National Park*
Source: Nagle, G., 1995, 'Killarney National Park', Geographical Magazine 67, 5, 61–3

QUESTIONS

1 a) In what ways does land ownership in British National Parks differ from those in Irish National Parks?

b) What are the implications of this for conservation?

2 Study Figure 6.17 which shows land-use zoning in Killarney National Park. Describe the pattern of zoning. How does this help conservation?

SUMMARY

In this chapter we have looked briefly at some of the ways in which landscapes are protected and managed. In some cases there is a definite conflict of interest between development and conservation. In others, notably where the land is owned by a conservation group, it is easier to balance conservation and development. We have seen how, in the Republic of Ireland, National Parks, are able to put conservation to the fore. By contrast, in British National Parks, most of the land is privately owned and this causes conflict between the needs of the owners and the aims of conservation groups. We have also seen that in small areas, such as Studland Beach and the Causeway coastline, it is easier to manage environments than when much larger areas are covered.

QUESTIONS

1 Outline the aims of Britain's National Parks. How successful have they been?
2 With the use of examples, outline the need for landscape conservation.
3 How can landscapes be managed? Give evidence to support your answer.

EXTENDED (PROJECT) WORK

Find out what types of landscape protection, such as national park status, AONB, SSSI, exist in your local area. You may need initial support from your teachers or from your local library or council office. Find out:
• what is being protected
• why it is considered of value
• how it is being protected
• how successful the schemes have been
• what local issues arise out of the protection of your chosen area.

BIBLIOGRAPHY AND RECOMMENDED READING

HMSO, 1994, Biodiversity, HMSO
Nagle, G., 1995, Killarney National Park, *Geographical magazine*, 67, 5, 61-3
Office of Public Works, 1990, *Killarney National Park management plan*, OPW
Smith, B. et al., 1994, *Footpath and visitor management strategy for the Causeway Coastal path network*, Department of the Environment (Northern Ireland) and Northern Ireland Tourist Board
Smith, B. and Ferris, C., 1997, Giant's Causeway: management of erosion hazard, *Geography review*, 11, 1, 30-7
Yorkshire Dales National Park, 1984, *National Park Plan*, Yorkshire Dales National Park
Yorkshire Dales National Park Committee, 1992, *Yorkshire Dales Visitor Study, 1991*, Yorkshire Dales National Park

WEB SITES

Trees for life -
http://www.gaia.org/treesforlife/
WWF – Global 2000
http://www.panda.org/livingplanet/spaces/space.htm
Envirolink -
http://www.envirolink.org/
English Nature -
http://www.english-nature.org.uk/

Glossary

Abiotic elements   Non-living elements such as air, water, heat, nutrients, rock and sediments.

Adiabatic processes   The change in temperature of a parcel of air caused by its ascent or descent i.e. there is no external source of heating or cooling; All changes are internal to the parcel of air.

Air mass   A large body of air with relatively uniform temperature and humidity characteristics.

Albedo   The reflectivity of the earth's surface.

Anticyclone   A high pressure system.

Atmosphere   The mixture of gases, predominantly nitrogen, oxygen, argon, carbon dioxide, and water vapour, that surrounds the earth.

Autotrophs   (or producers) Organisms capable of converting sunlit energy into food energy by photosynthesis.

Azonal soils   Immature or young soils which have not had time to develop characteristics related to bed rock or climate.

Bankfull discharge   The **discharge** measured when a river is at **bankfull stage**.

Bankfull stage   A condition in which a rivers channel fills completely, so that any further increase in discharge results in water overflowing the banks.

Base flow   The normal level of the river, is fed by groundwater.

Biogeography   is the geographic distribution of soils, vegetation and **ecosystems:** where they are and why they are there.

Biotic elements   Living elements such as plants and animals.

Calcification   A concentration of calcium in the soil where leaching is ineffective due to low rainfall.

Carnivores   Meat eaters.

Channelisation   Modifications to river channels, consisting of some combination of straightening, deepening, widening, clearing or lining of the natural channel.

Chelating agent   Humic acids

Cheluviation   The removal of the iron and aluminium sesquioxides from the soil under the influence of **chelating agents**.

Chemical weathering   The decomposition of rocks and minerals *in situ* as chemical reactions transform them into new chemical combinations that are stable at or near the earth's surface.

Climate   The average **weather** conditions of a place or an area over a period of not less than thirty years.

Climax community   The group of species that are at a dynamic equilibrium with the prevailing environmental conditions – for example in Britain this would be oak woodland under natural conditions.

Coriolis Force   An effect which causes any body that moves freely with respect to the rotating earth to travel to the right of its path in the Northern Hemisphere and to the left in the Southern Hemisphere.

Cyclone   An atmospheric low-pressure system that gives rise to roughly circular, inward-spiraling wind motion.

Detritivores   Decomposers.

Discharge   The quantity of water that passes a given point on the bank of a river within a given interval of time.

Drainage basin   The area drained by a river, for example, the Thames drainage basin or the Severn drainage basin.

Drought   An extended period of exceptionally low **precipitation**.

Ecosystem   The interrelationship between plants, animals, their living and non-living **environment**.

Environment   The biophysical system, in which people and other organisms exist; anything – living or non-living – that surrounds and influences living organisms.

Environmental lapse rate (ELR)   The normal decline of temperature with altitude - usually about 6°C / 1000 m.

Eutrophication   A process of nutrient enrichment, whereby the oxygen in water be-comes depleted as a result of the uncontrolled growth of plankton and algae.

Evaporation   The process which causes surface water to change into a gas.

Evapotranspiration   The combined loss of water from the soil and from plants by evapotranspiration and **evaporation**.

Front   A boundary between a warm air mass and a cold air mass, resulting in frontal (depressional or cyclonic) rainfall.

General circulation models   (GCMs) Climate models that portray interconnected processes in the atmosphere, hydros-phere, and biosphere.

Geostrophic wind   Air flow resulting from the combined effects of **pressure gradient forces** and Coriolis Force.

Gleyed soil A waterlogged soil.

Gradient wind Wind that blows from high pressure to low pressure.

Greenhouse effect The effect of the earth's atmosphere by which short-wave radiation from the sun is allowed to pass through the atmosphere and long-wave heat rays from the earth's surface are trapped or reflected back by the atmosphere.

Groundwater Water contained in spaces within bedrock and **regolith**.

Herbivores Plant eaters.

Heterotrophs Organisms that must feed on other organisms to survive.

Humidity A measure of the amount of moisture in the air. Absolute humidity is a measure of moisture in the air. Relative humidity expresses this amount as a percentage of the maximum water vapour that air at a particular temperature can hold.

Humification, **degradation** and **mineralisation** the process whereby organic matter is broken down and the nutrients are returned to the soil.

Humus Partially decomposed organic matter derived from the decay of dead plants and animals in soils.

Hydrology The study of water.

Hydrological cycle A natural cycle that describes the movement of water between land sea and atmosphere.

Illuviation The redeposition of material in the lower **soil horizons**.

Infiltration The process of water seeping into the ground.

Instability Unstable atmospheric conditions (usually leading to rising air) likely to cause cloud formation and **precipitation**.

Interception The process of **precipitation** being collected and stored by vegetation.

Intrazonal soils The intrazonal classification states that within a climatic zone soils vary with rock type.

Jet stream An intense thermal wind, found in the upper troposphere.

Lag time The time that elapses between the onset of **precipitation** and the **peak flow** stage.

Leaching The downward movement through the soil of soluble material in solution.

Load The particles of sediment and dissolved matter that are carried along by a river.

Net Primary Productivity The amount of energy made available by plants to **herbivores**.

Net Productivity The amount of energy remaining in an ecosystem after losses due to respiration, growth etc. are taken into account.

Omnivores Plant and meat eaters.

Overland run-off Water that flows over the land's surface.

Parent material The rock and mineral **regolith** from which soil develops.

Peak flow The maximum discharge of the river resulting from heavy precipitation.

Peat An unconsolidated deposit of partially decomposed plant remains with a carbon content of about 60 percent.

Permeability A measure of how easily a fluid passes through a solid.

Plagioclimax A plant community permanently influenced by man, i.e. prevented from reaching climatic climax by burning, or grazing etc.

Podsolisation An intense form of **leaching** involving the removal of sesquioxides under acidic conditions.

Porosity The percentage of the total volume of a body of regolith or bedrock that consists of open spaces or pores.

Precipitation moisture in any form i.e. rainfall, snow, frost, hail and dew. It is the conversion and transfer of moisture in the atmosphere to the land.

Pressure gradient force The force that causes air to move from high to low pressure.

Primary productivity Energy produced by plant productivity.

Prisere see **Succession**

Productivity refers to the rate of energy production in an ecosystem, normally on an annual basis.

Quick flow or **storm flow** The flow of storm water which flows into a river as a result of rapid **overland run-off**.

Recessional limb The part of a flood hydrograph that shows the speed with which the water level in the river declines after a peak, flow or flood.

Regolith Loose rock debris that covers the bedrock.

Rendzina A soil formed on chalk or limestone.

Rising limb The part of a flood hydrograph that shows how quickly flood waters rise.

River regime The annual variation in the flow of a river.

Run-off See *overland run-off*.

Salinisation   The upward movement of soluble salts in soil by capillary action, and their deposition in the surface horizons, forming a toxic crust.

Secondary Productivity   Energy in an ecosystem produced by animals.

Sere   Series of ecological communities formed in· succession. Each **sere** is an association or group of species, which alters the micro-environment and allows another group of species to dominate.

Soil fertility   The ability of a soil to provide the nutrients needed for plant growth.

Soil horizons   The distinguishable layers within a soil.

Soil profile   The succession of soil horizons between the surface and the underlying parent material.

Solar energy   Energy that reaches the earth from the sun.

Stability   Stable atmosphere conditions; with air unable to rise above a certain level; leading to calm, dry conditions, limited cloud formation.

Storm hydrograph   A graph showing how river flow changes over a short period, such as a day or a couple of days.

Subsidence   The sinking or collapse of a portion of the land surface.

Succession   The sequential changes in a community of plant species as it moves towards a **seral climax**.

Temperature inversion   A situation whereby warm air moves into an area and traps a pocket of cool air underneath it.

Time lag   The difference in time between the height of a storm and the peak flow in the river.

Transpiration   Water loss from vegetation to the atmosphere.

Tributary   A smaller river which joins up with a larger one.

Trophic system   classification of an ecosystem based on feeding patterns. Typically there is a trophic pyramid, with larger biomass of plants and less consumer biomass.

Water cycle   A movement of water between air, land and sea. It varies from place to place and over time.

Water table   The upper surface of the water in a saturated zone of ground.

Watershed   The dividing line between one drainage basin and another.

Weather   The state of the atmosphere at a given time and place, i.e. the pressure, wind, temperature, humidity, precipitation and cloud cover.

Weathering   The chemical alteration and physical breakdown of rock *in situ*.

Zonal soils   A classification of soil which states that on a global scale soils are determined by climate.

Index

Dedication – To Rosie, Patrick and Bethany

Acknowledgements
The author and publishers are grateful to the following for permission to reproduce copyright photographs:
Hulton Getty: figures 2.5 and 3.18
Nigel Dickinson/Still Pictures: figure 3.2
Leslie Garland Picture Library: 3.13
Spectrum Colour Library: figures 3.27 and 6.8
Chris Fairclough Colour Library: figure 5.22
Planet Earth Pictures: figure 5.26
Images Colour Library: figure 6.6
Sean Ryan: Figure 5.11
B. J. Smith, Department of Geosciences, Queen's University Belfast: figures 6.14 and 6.15

All other photographs by Garrett Nagle.

Every effort has been made to trace all the relevant copyright holders, but if any have been inadvertly overlooked, the publishers will be pleased to make the necessary arrangements at the first opportunity.

The author would like to thank the many people who have given so much help, in particular Christine Berry, Betty Morgan, Misia Newsome and Gill Yeomans. And to Angela, Patrick and Rosie for being so patient and helpful.

Thomas Nelson & Sons Ltd
Nelson House
Mayfield Road
Walton-on-Thames
Surrey KT12 5PL
United Kingdom

Picture Research by Image Select International Ltd
Page make-up and illustration by Pentacor, High Wycombe, Buckinghamshire, UK
Printed by Zrinski Printing & Publishing House, Cakovec, Croatia

Project management by Sue Mildenhall
Cover design by Liam Reardon